SCIENCE
LEVEL FIVE
SECOND EDITION

Science Notebook

purposeful design®
p u b l i c a t i o n s

Colorado Springs, Colorado

Elementary Science, Level Five – Science Notebook
Purposeful Design Elementary Science series
ISBN 978-1-58331-536-1, Catalog #20053

Purposeful Design Publications is the publishing division of the Association of Christian Schools International (ACSI) and is committed to the ministry of Christian school education, to enable Christian educators and schools worldwide to effectively prepare students for life. As the publisher of textbooks, trade books, and other educational resources within ACSI, Purposeful Design Publications strives to produce biblically sound materials that reflect Christian scholarship and stewardship and that address the identified needs of Christian schools around the world.

References to books, computer software, and other ancillary resources in this series are not endorsements by ACSI. These materials were selected to provide teachers with additional resources appropriate to the concepts being taught and to promote student understanding and enjoyment.

All Scripture quotations in this publication, unless otherwise noted, are taken from the HOLY BIBLE, NEW INTERNATIONAL VERSION ® (NIV) ® Copyright © 1973, 1978, and 1984 by Biblica, Inc.®. All rights reserved worldwide.

Dawn®, **4.7A**, is a registered trademark of Procter & Gamble, which does not authorize, sponsor, or endorse this textbook.
Tectonic plates, **9.3A**, NOAA/Department of Commerce
Nutrition facts labels, **13.6A**, US Department of Agriculture

Purposeful Design Publications
A Division of ACSI
731 Chapel Hills Drive • Colorado Springs, CO • 80920
Customer Service Department: 800-367-0798 • Website: www.purposefuldesign.com

Name _____

Keep It Going

Follow the directions below to complete the activities. Record your observations and answer any questions.

1. Stand in a straight line with your group. Place the container of plastic game pieces at one end of the line. Place an empty container at the other end.

2. The person nearest the container of game pieces should take one piece and pass it down the line. The person on the other end should deposit the game piece into the empty container. Repeat this process until all of the game pieces have been passed down the line in the same direction and placed into the container.

3. If you pass the game pieces down the line at a rate of one piece per second, can you keep the pieces going for one minute? Why or why not?

_____

_____

4. In your group, devise a way to pass the game pieces at the rate of one piece per second for two minutes. Describe your method below. What had to change in order for you to keep the process going for two minutes?

_____

_____

_____

_____

5. Compare and contrast the two activities. What was similar? What was different?

_____

_____

_____

_____

_____

6. How might these activities model the way that nutrients are transferred in an ecosystem? Which model better represents an ecosystem—the model using a straight line or the model you devised?

_____

_____

_____

_____

1.1B
NOTEBOOK

Name _____

Recycle Paper

Follow the directions below to complete the activity. Answer the questions.

1. Place the wire mesh into your pie pan and then place the pie pan on top of all but one of your paper towels.

2. After your teacher places the pulp on your wire mesh, spread it evenly over the screen with your fingers. Hold the wire mesh over your pie pan until the water has completely drained.

3. Carefully set aside the pie pan and place the wire mesh directly on the paper towels. Place one fresh paper towel over the pulp. Use the rolling pin to flatten the pulp further and to force out the water. Remove the wet paper towels. Transfer the mesh to the location selected by your teacher. Allow the pulp to dry completely.

4. List three things that you know are recyclable:

   a. _____ b. _____ c. _____

5. Why do people recycle paper and other materials?

   _____

   _____

   _____

   _____

   _____

   _____

6. How is recycling paper similar to how an ecosystem recycles nutrients? How is it different?

   _____

   _____

   _____

   _____

   _____

21

Name _____

Water Cycle in a Jar

Use the materials you are given to construct a water cycle in a jar. Write a question to be answered and a hypothesis of what you think will happen when ice cubes are placed on the lid of the jar filled with hot water.

Question: What do you want to know?

1. _____

Hypothesize: What do you think the answer will be?

2. _____

Test It: Your teacher will pour hot water into your jar. Immediately place the lid on the jar and tightly seal it. Then place ice cubes on the top of the lid.

Record and Analyze: Use a timer to observe the sides of the jar after one, two, and three minutes.

3. Record your observations in the chart and complete the exercise below.

time	observations
1 minute	
2 minutes	
3 minutes	

4. Describe what happened in your jar.

_____

_____

_____

Conclude: How do the results compare to your hypothesis?

5. _____

_____

_____

Share: Find a partner and share what you learned from this experiment.

Name _____

Analyze the Cycle

Using your observations from **Science Notebook 1.3A Water Cycle in a Jar**, answer the questions and complete the exercises below.

1. What was the purpose of having the ice on top of the lid?

_____

_____

_____

_____

2. Your teacher used electricity or an open flame to warm the water and power the experiment in the jar. What supplies the energy to power the water cycle in nature?

_____

3. List three ways that the jar experiment accurately modeled what happens in the natural water cycle.

a. _____

_____

b. _____

_____

c. _____

_____

4. List three ways that the jar experiment differed from the natural water cycle.

a. _____

_____

b. _____

_____

c. _____

_____

Name _____

Microscope Structure

Write the name of the correct term for each part of this microscope on the line provided. Use the words in the Word Bank.

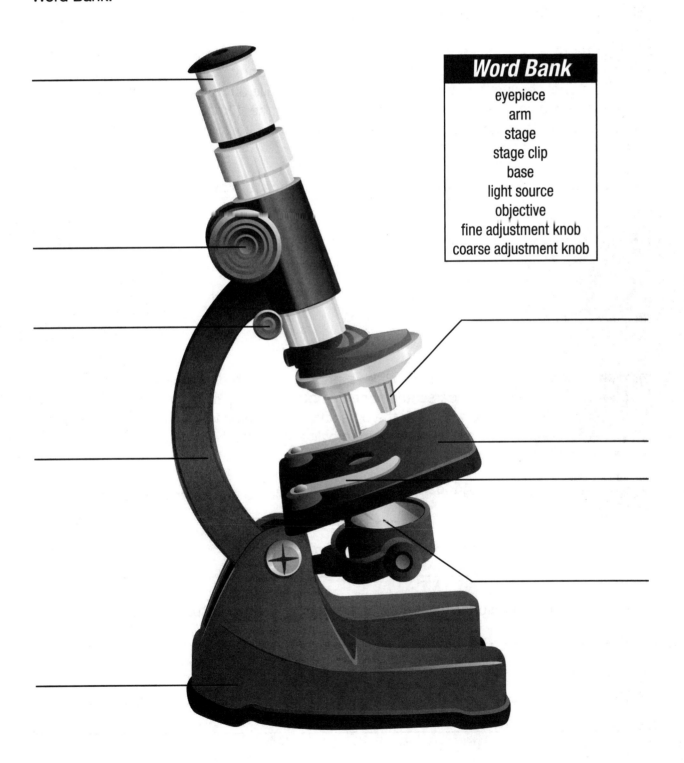

Name _____

Microscope Practice

Use the slide your teacher has given you to practice focusing the microscope. Complete the steps and answer the questions below.

1. Gently slip the slide under the stage clips so that the objective is directly over the tape.

2. First, use the low power objective (the shortest one) to view the slide. Turn the coarse adjustment knob to lower the objective until it is just above the slide. Be careful not to touch the slide with the objective. They are both fragile and may crack. While looking into the eyepiece, very slowly turn the coarse adjustment knob, moving the objective upward. A clear image should come into view. Note: if your image is not clear enough, you may need to use the fine adjustment knob.

3. Observe. With a pencil, draw what you see in the space provided below.

4. With the objective high above the slide, switch to the high power objective (the longest one). Lower it using the coarse adjustment knob until it is just above the slide. Be careful not to touch the slide with the objective. While looking into the eyepiece, very slowly turn the coarse adjustment knob, moving the objective upward. A clear image should come into view.

5. Is there any difference between what you drew in Step 3 and what you saw in Step 4? If so, describe it.

_____

_____

6. Describe why microscopes are important and how to properly use them.

_____

_____

_____

_____

Name _____

How Plants Breathe

Follow the steps below to make and observe a leaf slide. Draw your observations in the space provided.

Making Your Slide

1. Turn your leaf so that the underside is facing up. Use clear fingernail polish to paint a patch about the size of your thumbprint on the bottom of the leaf. Let the fingernail polish dry completely.

2. Cut a small piece of clear tape about twice the length of the patch you just painted. Press the center of the tape firmly against the patch of fingernail polish. Be careful not to get your fingerprints in the middle of the tape.

3. Start at one edge of the tape and carefully peel it off the leaf. The patch of fingernail polish should come off with the tape. If it does not, repeat Steps 1–3 until it does.

4. Press the tape with the patch onto a clean microscope slide.

Observing Your Slide

1. Place your leaf slide under the lens of the microscope. Your teacher has already positioned the lens for you. Make sure that the slide is directly under the lens.

2. Look through the microscope. If the slide is out of focus, carefully turn the adjustment knob(s) to improve the view. If you are still having trouble, ask your teacher for help.

3. Look for structures that are similar to tiny mouths. The cells that look like lips are called *guard cells*. They surround a hole called the *stoma,* which means *opening*. Carbon dioxide enters the leaf through these stomata. (*Stomata* is the plural of stoma.) The cells that surround the guard cells should look like pieces of a jigsaw puzzle. They are called *epidermal cells*. If you cannot identify the guard cells, stomata, and epidermal cells, ask your teacher for help.

From your observations, draw a small section of the leaf using a pencil. Draw lines to label the guard cells, stomata, and epidermal cells. Your lines should not crisscross.

1.4D
NOTEBOOK

Name ______________________________

How Plants Breathe, continued

Use your textbook and your observations to complete the exercises.

1. Draw the carbon and oxygen cycle below. Use arrows to label how these elements move from biotic to abiotic components and back again.

2. Describe the structure that plants use to breathe.

____

____

3. For what process do plants use carbon dioxide? Summarize the process.

____

____

____

____

4. Describe how carbon gets from the atmosphere into a carnivore.

____

____

____

____

Name _____

Label the Cycle

Identify the parts of the nitrogen cycle shown in the picture. Cut out and paste the labels you have been given next to the correct image.

Name _____

Fertilizer

Read the paragraph and the label below. Use the information to complete the exercises.

Organisms thrive in ecosystems where all the elements they need are abundant. When these elements decrease, growth and reproduction become limited. When farmers harvest their crops, they remove the plants from the fields. This prevents the plants from decomposing. Nutrients are not returned to the soil. Plants need nitrogen to build proteins and phosphorus for energy and storage. Potassium is also necessary for transportation of fluids across and within cells. In order to use the field again, farmers may need to add fertilizers with these and other elements in order to make the soil fertile once again.

General Purpose Fertilizer
20-10-20

Nitrogen (N)	20%
Phosphorus (P)	10%
Potassium (K)	20%
Magnesium (Mg)	0.05%
Boron (B)	0.0068%
Copper (Cu)	0.0036%
Iron (Fe)	0.05%
Manganese (Mn)	0.025%
Molybdenum (Mo)	0.0009%
Zinc (Zn)	0.0025%

1. Which three elements are present in the greatest amounts? Why?

_____

_____

2. Why do farmers need to fertilize their fields?

_____

_____

3. Some farmers spread the waste from livestock, called *manure*, on their fields instead of chemical fertilizers. The animal waste is rich in elements. What do you think happens to the manure once it is spread on the field?

_____

_____

Name _____

An Experimental Forest

Read the paragraph and use the information to answer the questions.

Located in the US state of New Hampshire is a bowl-shaped valley in the White Mountain National Forest. In 1955 this area was set aside so that scientists could study the forest, soil, and water that flowed from six nearly identical watersheds. The forest is called the *Hubbard Brook Experimental Forest*. The scientists were interested in changes that might occur in the biogeochemical cycles when humans disturb the forest. The forest in Watershed 6 was left undisturbed. It was called a *reference watershed*. Scientists would conduct experiments on the other five watersheds and compare them to Watershed 6 to see what effects their experiments had. In 1966 scientists did something dramatic to Watershed 2. They experimented by cutting down all the trees in this watershed and spraying chemicals to prevent plants from growing. Then they sampled the water that flowed from Watersheds 2 and 6 and compared them. They discovered that Watershed 2 had too much nitrate in the water. Nitrate is a nitrogen-retaining molecule. This indicated that nitrogen was no longer being cycled through the soil, plants, and animals. Instead, this important element was being lost from the ecosystem. In 1969 scientists at Hubbard Brook Experimental Forest decided to allow the forest to start growing again.

1. What did scientists do to the forest in Watershed 6? Why was it called the *reference watershed*?

_____

_____

2. Why do scientists need a reference when they are conducting an experiment?

_____

_____

3. What did scientists do to the forest in Watershed 2? What effects did it have on the nitrogen cycle in the area?

_____

_____

_____

4. Why do you think Watershed 2 lost more nitrogen than Watershed 6?

_____

_____

Name _____

Disrupting the Nitrogen Cycle

Use the information in the box below to draw a double line graph that shows the amount of nitrate in the water of both watersheds. Use blue to mark Watershed 6 and red to mark Watershed 2.

	1965	1966	1967	1968
Watershed 6 nitrate levels (mg/L)	0.51	0.54	0.60	0.91
Watershed 2 nitrate levels (mg/L)	0.61	21.80	53.75	48.88

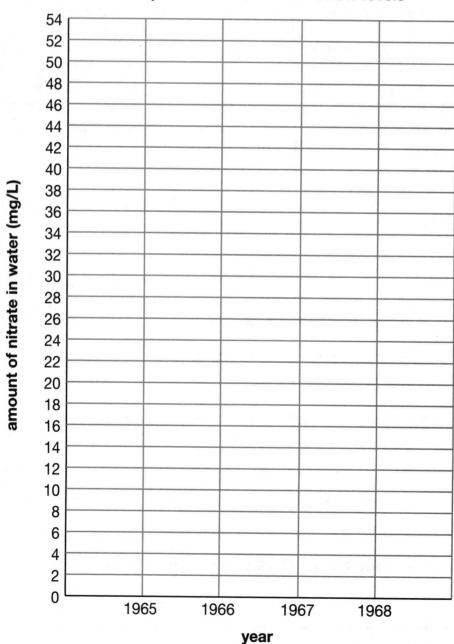

comparison of watershed nitrate levels

Name _____

Interpret the Graph

Use the information from the graph on **Science Notebook 1.6B Disrupting the Nitrogen Cycle** to answer the questions below.

1. Why is the year 1966 significant to Watershed 2? _____

_____

_____

2. Which watershed lost more nitrogen in 1967? _____

3. According to the graph, what happens to the nitrogen in a forest ecosystem when the trees are cut down and the remaining plants are killed?

_____

_____

4. If the forest in Watershed 2 were allowed to grow back, what would happen to the amount of nitrogen being lost?

_____

_____

_____

_____

5. Describe how a loss of nitrogen could affect an ecosystem. What could be done to restore it?

_____

_____

_____

_____

_____

_____

_____

_____

Name _____

Test Acids

Follow the steps in the activity below, complete the exercises, and answer the questions.

Question: How does acid affect other substances?

Hypothesize: What might happen when vinegar is added to the acid indicator?

1. _____

Test It: Observe as your teacher adds the vinegar.

Record and Analyze: Describe what you see. Was your hypothesis correct?

2. _____

_____

3. Predict what will happen when your teacher blows into the indicator. _____

_____

4. Observe as your teacher blows into the indicator. Describe what you see. Was your

   hypothesis correct? _____

_____

5. Why did the vinegar change the indicator more than when your teacher blew into it?

_____

6. Why was it necessary to keep an unused cup of indicator nearby? _____

_____

_____

Conclude: What does this experiment indicate about how carbon dioxide interacts
with water? What might happen if rainwater becomes a strong acid?

7. _____

_____

_____

_____

Share: Tell a classmate what you learned from your experiment.

Name _____

Chalk Talk

Follow the steps below to finish the experiment. Record your observations and complete the exercises.

1. Pour 60 mL ($\frac{1}{4}$ cup) of water into one cup and 60 mL ($\frac{1}{4}$ cup) of vinegar into a second cup.

2. Use a paper clip to scrape the sides of a piece of chalk in several places. Break the chalk in two and place a piece into each cup. Observe for one minute.

3. Record your observations.

Chalk in Water

_____

_____

Chalk in Vinegar

_____

_____

4. What would happen to the chalk in both containers if they were left there for several days? Why?

_____

_____

_____

_____

5. What does this experiment demonstrate about acid precipitation? What effects does acid precipitation have on living things?

_____

_____

_____

_____

_____

_____

1.7B
NOTEBOOK

Name _____

Pass a Law

Imagine you are the leader of your country. Design three laws that you could pass that would help prevent photochemical smog and acid precipitation. Describe the laws, their effects, and any opposition you may encounter.

1. Law 1

_____

_____

Effects

_____

_____

2. Law 2

_____

_____

Effects

_____

_____

3. Law 3

_____

_____

Effects

_____

_____

4. What might people say to oppose the three laws you designed? How would you respond?

_____

_____

_____

_____

Name _____

Vocabulary Review

Use each of the following words in a sentence or sentences that demonstrates your understanding of the definition. Give an example of where each term could be found.

1. acid precipitation

_____

_____

2. nodule

_____

_____

3. denitrification

_____

_____

4. cellular respiration

_____

_____

5. fossil fuel

_____

_____

6. collection

_____

_____

7. nitrogen fixation

_____

_____

8. photochemical smog

_____

_____

9. emission

_____

_____

10. runoff

_____

_____

Name _____

Chapter 1 Review

Write the names of three biogeochemical cycles on the lines below. In the spaces provided, illustrate and label the parts of each cycle.

1. _____

2. _____

3. _____

4. Name the four elements that are most abundant in living things.

_____ _____ _____ _____

Name _____

Chapter 1 Review, continued

Complete the exercises and answer the questions below. Write complete sentences.

5. Describe the process of photosynthesis. How do both photosynthesis and cellular respiration fit into the carbon and oxygen cycle?

_____

_____

_____

_____

6. Name an example of a legume. Describe its importance to an ecosystem.

_____

_____

7. Use the words in the Word Bank to label the parts of the microscope below.

Word Bank
arm
coarse adjustment knob
base
stage clip
light source
objective
stage
fine adjustment knob
eyepiece

8. Describe why a microscope is an important tool and how to use one properly.

_____

_____

_____

_____

Name _____

Chapter 1 Review, continued

Read the following paragraph. Then follow the directions below.

A small town in a forested area is having problems. Many people cannot find jobs in the town. The mayor of the town has decided to call a town meeting where several ideas will be presented. One citizen, Mr. Evets, wants to cut down a large section of the forest and build an amusement park to attract tourists and people from the surrounding towns. The park will create more jobs for the town's citizens. It may even bring in more business to the town's restaurants and parks. Another citizen, Mr. Nod, wants to build several small campgrounds in the forest and connect them by making trails. The campground will allow visitors to hike, go rafting, and camp in the forest. It will also offer cross-country skiing and horseback riding during the winter months. The campground will create additional jobs and bring extra business to the town.

Pretend that you will be attending the town meeting to give a speech. Record what you would say. Include which idea you think will be better for the townspeople and for the surrounding ecosystem. Include any other recommendations you have for how the town can improve its economy. Defend your decision.

_____

_____

_____

_____

_____

_____

_____

_____

_____

_____

_____

_____

_____

_____

Name _____

Human Life Cycle Diagram

Cut out pictures of people in various stages of life. Arrange the images in whatever pattern your group chooses and glue them to the poster board. Use a marker to label each picture with one of the stages listed in the Word Bank. Be sure to title the poster and to include the names of each group member. Then answer the questions that follow.

Note: For the unborn human or prenatal stage, you could look for a picture of an expectant mother.

| **Word Bank** | unborn human | older adult | toddler (1–3 years) | infant |
| | young adult | teenager (13–19 years) | child | |

1. Explain why you arranged the pictures on your group's poster in a particular pattern.

_____

_____

_____

2. How could these pictures be arranged to show a cycle?

_____

_____

_____

3. Are all human life cycles alike? How do they sometimes differ?

_____

_____

_____

_____

4. List three ways people change during the human life cycle.

a. _____

_____

b. _____

_____

c. _____

_____

Name _____

My Early Life and Beyond

Match the descriptions of each human life stage to the correct picture by placing the letter of the image next to its description below. Then follow the rest of the directions below.

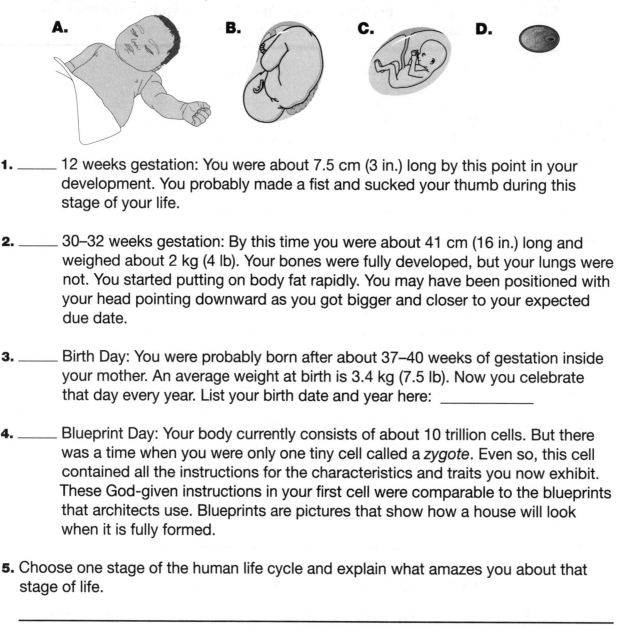

A.   **B.**   **C.**   **D.**

1. _____ 12 weeks gestation: You were about 7.5 cm (3 in.) long by this point in your development. You probably made a fist and sucked your thumb during this stage of your life.

2. _____ 30–32 weeks gestation: By this time you were about 41 cm (16 in.) long and weighed about 2 kg (4 lb). Your bones were fully developed, but your lungs were not. You started putting on body fat rapidly. You may have been positioned with your head pointing downward as you got bigger and closer to your expected due date.

3. _____ Birth Day: You were probably born after about 37–40 weeks of gestation inside your mother. An average weight at birth is 3.4 kg (7.5 lb). Now you celebrate that day every year. List your birth date and year here: _____

4. _____ Blueprint Day: Your body currently consists of about 10 trillion cells. But there was a time when you were only one tiny cell called a *zygote*. Even so, this cell contained all the instructions for the characteristics and traits you now exhibit. These God-given instructions in your first cell were comparable to the blueprints that architects use. Blueprints are pictures that show how a house will look when it is fully formed.

5. Choose one stage of the human life cycle and explain what amazes you about that stage of life.

_____

_____

6. Predict at least one way the world might be different when you are old enough to be a grandparent.

_____

_____

Name _____

Spore Prints and Mushroom Parts

1. Write your name on a piece of white paper.
2. Gently pull the stem off your mushroom and expose the gills.
3. Set the mushroom down on the piece of white paper so that the gills are against the paper.
4. Allow the mushroom and paper to be undisturbed for about three days.
5. After three days, carefully lift the mushroom from the paper. You should see a spore print.
6. Your teacher will help you spray your print with hairspray so that the spores stick to the paper.
7. Draw a mushroom below and label its four main parts.

Name _____

Classroom Fungi

Spores from fungi are everywhere—even in your classroom! Follow the directions below and answer the questions in approximately three days.

1. Take your slice of bread and find a particularly dusty place in your classroom. Tops of cabinets, baseboards, and window sills are good options.
2. Gently wipe one side of the bread slice in the dust.
3. Moisten the same side of the bread with one squirt of water from the spray bottle.
4. Place the slice of bread in a ziplock bag and store it in a warm, dark place.
5. In a few days, take a look at your bread, but do not open the bag. Simply look at the bread through the plastic bag.
6. Describe what you observe.

_____

_____

_____

7. Where had you wiped your bread slice?

_____

_____

_____

8. How do you think the fungal spores got into your classroom?

_____

_____

_____

9. What conditions did the fungus need in order to grow?

_____

_____

_____

10. Why are fungi not growing all over your classroom?

_____

_____

Name _____

Seed Germination

Obtain the materials for this activity from your teacher. Follow the directions below, draw your observations, and answer the questions.

1. Fold your paper towels into fourths. They should now be square-shaped. Wet your paper towels. Fold the squares in half. This will make them rectangular in shape. Squeeze out most of the water.
2. Carefully unfold the rectangles to form the squares again. Place one paper towel inside each of your small ziplock bags. Write your name on your bag using a marker.
3. Put three bean seeds on top of each paper towel inside the bag and do not let them touch each other. Push most of the air out of your bags and seal the tops.
4. Store your bags where your teacher tells you to—one in a warm, dark place and one in a warm, bright place.
5. Check your seeds every day, but do not open the bags. The first day you see a change in one of your seeds, draw it here.

6. What part of the seed embryo started growing first? _____

7. Draw that same seed every day after you see a change.

8. What conditions did your seed need to germinate?

_____

9. Which conditions helped your seeds to grow better and faster?

_____

10. Describe what happened to the seeds that were in darkness.

_____

11. Did anyone's seeds fail to germinate? If so, what may have been a reason why those seeds did not germinate?

_____

Name _____

A Closer Look

Using the materials your teacher has given you, follow the directions to inspect your flower. Use the diagram of flower parts in your textbook to help complete the exercises below.

1. Lay the flower on the piece of white construction paper.

2. Write the name of the flower you are observing.

_____

3. Find the petals and sepals. How many petals and sepals does your flower have? Remember that sepals do not always stay green and may be the same color as the petals. The sepals surround the bottom part of the flower.

_____ petals   _____ sepals

4. Carefully pull all the sepals and petals off the flower. You should be left with only the structures in the center of the flower.

5. Look at the long structures in the center of your flower. Most of them look similar.

What are these structures called? _____

6. Brush your finger over the surfaces of the top parts of those structures. You may be able to see some pollen clinging to your finger or falling off the anthers. Each pollen grain carries one-half of what?

_____

7. An anther is attached to a long stalk. What is it called? _____

8. How many anthers does your flower have? _____

9. Gently pull off all the anthers and the stalks attached to them. There should be another long structure left standing that does not have an anther on top. What is it called?

_____

10. Use your plastic knife to cut the ovary in half, lengthwise. (The ovary is the structure at the base of the long structure in Step 9.) Begin where the flower meets the stem and gently slice all the way up through the stigma. Carefully look for very small structures inside the ovary. Inside each one is an egg that contains the other half of what the pollen contains. What does the egg contain? _____

11. Can you see the tiny structures that hold eggs inside the plant's ovary?_____

Name _____

Salmon Habitats

Place the letter or letters of the appropriate habitat under the name of each salmon life stage. Some stages will need more than one because of the complex nature of the salmon's life cycle. Then write at least one fact about each stage.

a. stream	**b. ocean**	**c. river**

1. redd _____

_____

_____

2. smolt _____

_____

_____

3. alevin _____

_____

_____

4. parr _____

_____

_____

5. adult _____

_____

_____

Name _____

My Life as a Salmon

Write a paragraph or two about the salmon life cycle from the point of view of a salmon. Choose a name for yourself and remember to write in the first person voice. Use all four vocabulary words from this lesson, as well as the other life stages listed in your textbook diagram. Also, be sure to mention where each stage lives and develops. Be creative!

_____

_____

_____

_____

_____

_____

_____

_____

_____

_____

_____

_____

_____

_____

_____

_____

_____

_____

_____

_____

Name _____

Variables

Read the following paragraphs and answer the questions.

The scientific inquiry process begins with asking a question. Then a hypothesis is made. An investigation or experiment must take place to know if the prediction was correct. During an experiment, there are many variables or factors that can change. For instance, if the effect of air temperature on plant growth was being investigated, the temperature of the air, the kind of plant, the soil type, and the amounts of water and sunlight would be some of the variables. One way to ensure that the results of the experiment are accurate is to test only one variable at a time. In this case, the air temperature will be the one factor that is intentionally changed. This factor is known as the *independent variable*.

The factors that do not change in an experiment are called *controlled variables*. Examples of controlled variables in the investigation above would be to use the same type of plant and soil and the same amounts of water and sunlight. If only one independent variable is tested, such as the air temperature, then it is possible to determine how that factor affects plant growth. If more than one independent variable is changed, then it is difficult to accurately conclude which factor affects plant growth. The factor that may be affected and then changed in response to the independent variable is called the *dependent variable*. Since the effect of air temperature on plant growth is being tested, the dependent variable in this particular experiment is plant growth.

For the experiment below, identify the independent, dependent, and controlled variables.

A study was done to find out how much a rabbit's appetite would be affected by exercise. The same rabbit was used for each trial. The amount of exercise the rabbit performed changed with each trial. The amount of food the rabbit ate was measured.

1. What was the independent variable? _____

2. What was the dependent variable? _____

3. What variable was controlled? _____

Hatching Brine Shrimp

Divide into groups and obtain a brine shrimp hatching kit from your teacher. Write the initials of your group members on both of the jars. Label one jar with a *1*, and the other jar with a *2*. You will be performing an investigation. Keep in mind the types of variables involved as you experiment to answer the following main question:

Question: In what type of environment do brine shrimp thrive?

Name _____

Hatching Brine Shrimp, *continued*

Follow the directions and complete the exercises below.

Jar 1:

1. Add a level teaspoon of salt to Jar 1. Stir the water to dissolve the salt. The saltwater that each group makes for Jar 1 is a(n) _____ variable.

   Explain why. _____

Jar 2:

2. With your group decide on the environment of a second jar of water. Circle one:
   - make the water acidic by adding vinegar
   - make the water saltier by adding more salt
   - keep the water as is without adding vinegar or salt

3. What kind of variables are these? _____

   Explain why. _____

4. The brine shrimp are the _____ variable in this investigation.

Hypothesize: Predict how the environment in your Jar 2 will affect the number of cysts that hatch. Circle one.

   increase   decrease   has no affect

5. Find a group that made a different choice for Jar 2's environment.
   Circle what they chose.

   acid (vinegar)   more salt   no salt or vinegar

6. Predict whether your group or the other group's second jar will hatch more

   brine shrimp. _____ Why? _____

7. Ask your teacher to do one of the following to Jar 2: Circle one.
   - add 5mL (1 tsp) vinegar   • add 5mL (1 tsp) salt   • add neither salt nor vinegar

Test It:

8. Into both jars add a small pinch of brine shrimp cysts and screw on the lids.

9. Record today's date and the time you placed the cysts in the jars. _____

10. Observe your group's jars now, tomorrow, and the day after, filling out **Science Notebook 2.6C Observation of Brine Shrimp** each time.

Name _____

Observation of Brine Shrimp

Record your observations of the brine shrimp jars. Analyze variables such as water color, water level, amounts of cysts or nauplii, location of cysts or nauplii, and location of jars.

Test It, continued:

	jar 1	jar 2	date and time
right now	a. _____ _____ b. _____ _____	a. _____ _____ b. _____ _____	_____ _____
one day later	a. _____ _____ b. _____ _____	a. _____ _____ b. _____ _____	_____ _____
two days later	a. _____ _____ b. _____ _____	a. _____ _____ b. _____ _____	_____ _____

1. Did the brine shrimp hatch in Jar 1, Jar 2, both jars, or neither of the jars?

_____

2. Were there more nauplii in Jar 1 or Jar 2? _____

3. Compare your Jar 2 to the other group's Jar 2. Which group has more hatched shrimp

in Jar 2? _____

Name _____

Conclusions About Brine Shrimp

Complete the following exercises:

Analyze and Conclude:

1. Compare your group's brine shrimp jars. Circle the answer that best completes the statement.

   Jar 1 was _____ than Jar 2.

   a. more acidic   **b.** more salty   **c.** less acidic / less salty

2. Approximately how many hours or days did it take for the cysts to hatch in

   Jar 1? _____ Jar 2? _____ the other groups' Jar 2? _____

3. Did either group's brine shrimp fail to hatch? If so, which group and which jar?

   _____

4. What differences, if any, did you notice in Jar 1 between the first and second days after your experiment set-up day?

   _____

   _____

5. What differences, if any, did you notice in Jar 2 between the first and second days after your experiment set-up day?

   _____

   _____

6. What differences, if any, did you notice in the other groups' Jar 2 between the first and second days after your experiment set-up day?

   _____

   _____

7. According to the results you have observed and recorded, what are the best environmental conditions for hatching brine shrimp?

   _____

   _____

8. List three other variables in the environment that might have affected the hatching of your brine shrimp.

   a. _____   **c.** _____

   b. _____

Combating Malaria

Malaria-carrying *Anopheles* mosquitoes tend to be active at dawn, dusk, and during the night in hot and humid countries. Most people affected by malaria are uneducated or too poor to buy the proper medicine. Keeping these facts in mind, follow the directions and complete the exercises below. Remember to only use the Internet with a parent or guardian's permission.

One way to fight malaria is to try to get rid of the infected mosquitoes by spraying insecticides.

1. Other than spraying insecticides, name one thing you would do, if you had the resources, to help prevent people from getting sick with malaria.

_____

_____

2. With the help of your parent or guardian, use the Internet to perform a general search under the keyword *malaria*. List three things that individuals or governments have done to slow the spread of this disease.

a. _____

b. _____

c. _____

3. Using the Internet, find out whether there are ever cases of malaria in the United States. (The U.S. government's Centers for Disease Control and Prevention may be a helpful site.) Record the results of your research here.

_____

_____

4. Write three interesting facts that you discovered about malaria from your online search or from other sources.

a. _____

b. _____

c. _____

Name _____

The Anopheles Mosquito

Read the paragraphs, label the image, and follow the directions. You may use outside resources if necessary.

The *Anopheles gambiae*, one of about 430 species of the *Anopheles* mosquitoes, is the major malaria-carrying one. Like other mosquitoes, it has a four-stage life cycle—egg, larva, pupa, and adult. In the adult stage, the *Anopheles* insect has a slender body with three main sections—head, thorax, and abdomen. Its head has a long, straw-like proboscis, which is used to puncture the skin of humans and animals to obtain a blood meal. This blood meal helps the female's eggs to mature. It has feathery antennas, as well. The antennae help detect the odor of the insect's victims and its breeding grounds for laying eggs.

Characteristics that would distinguish it from other mosquitoes are its two sensory structures, called *palps,* and its unique wing design. The palps are located on either side of the proboscis and can be almost as long as the proboscis. They allow the mosquito to sense nearby levels of carbon dioxide, helping it find a victim for its blood meal. Its wings contain blocks of black and white scales. The mosquito's hum comes from the beating of these wings. The *Anopheles'* resting position is also different than other species. They stick their abdomens up in the air instead of keeping them parallel to the surface on which they are resting.

1. Label the three main sections of the mosquito's body.
2. Label its long proboscis.
3. Label the feathery antennae.
4. Label the sensory palps.

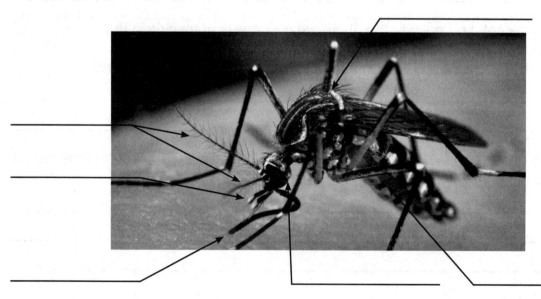

Name _____

Vocabulary Review

Write the number of the word on the blank next to its definition.

1. genetic material

_____ a young plant

2. generation

_____ a fleshy, spore-producing growth of certain fungi

3. mushroom

_____ a plant structure that surrounds the seeds of flowering plants

4. redd

_____ a very young salmon hatchling

5. cotyledon

_____ an organism produced from a spore or fertilized egg, in the early stages of development

6. alevin

_____ a salmon nest

7. smolt

_____ the nutrient-rich structure in a seed

8. fruit

_____ one complete life cycle

9. fertilization

_____ the uniting of the genetic material of two cells

10. embryo

_____ an immature salmon that migrates to the ocean

11. seedling

_____ the set of instructions within a cell that controls an organism's characteristics and life processes

Name _____

Chapter 2 Review

1. Draw a fungal life cycle. Label the different stages of the life cycle.

2. Draw a flowering plant life cycle. Label the different stages of the life cycle.

2.8C
NOTEBOOK

Chapter 2 Review, continued

3. Draw a mushroom and label the cap, stem, and gills.

4. What are the best type of places for a fungus to grow? Circle two.

a. dry   **b.** warm   **c.** cold   **d.** moist

5. Draw a flower and label the following parts: *sepal*, *petal*, *ovary*, *anther*, and *stigma*.

6. Describe the function of each of the following plant structures:

pollen: _____

fruit: _____

cotyledons: _____

embryo: _____

7. What do pollinators do and how is this helpful in the life cycle of a flowering plant?

_____

_____

_____

Name _____

Chapter 2 Review, continued

8. Explain how unicellular bacteria reproduce. _____

_____

_____

9. Bacteria can be found in many places on Earth. Name three.

    a. _____

    b. _____

    c. _____

10. Suppose you opened up a loaf of bread this morning only to find that there was mold growing on it. How did the mold most likely get on the bread?

_____

_____

11. The saltwater in Jar 1 of the brine shrimp experiment was a _____

variable. What was the dependent variable? _____

12. What were the three options for independent variables for Jar 2 in the brine

shrimp experiment? _____

_____

13. Name at least three stages of the salmon's life cycle. _____

_____

14. List two ways that humans sometimes interfere with the life cycle of the salmon.

_____

_____

15. What is a fish ladder? _____

_____

16. What disease is caused by the one-celled *Plasmodium* parasite? _____

17. What insect transmits this disease to humans? _____

Name _____

Puzzling

Obtain a bag of puzzle pieces from your teacher. Assemble the pieces to complete the image. Answer the questions and complete the exercises below.

1. Is your puzzle complete? _____ If so, proceed to Question 3. If something is missing or does not fit, discuss as a group how you can solve this problem. When you come up with a prediction, record it here.

_____

2. Try out your prediction. Develop other possible ideas until you are able to complete the puzzle. Write the name of the object in your puzzle here.

_____

3. Describe the object in your puzzle the best that you can. What is its purpose? Describe how it is used.

_____

_____

4. What are some of the individual parts that make up this object?

_____

_____

5. Do any of the individual parts move? Are the moving parts necessary for the object to work?

_____

_____

_____

_____

6. Similar to the transportation vehicle pictured on your puzzle, living things also have many moving parts that work together to allow the organism to work or survive. These smaller parts are called *cells*. Write what you know about cells.

_____

_____

_____

Name _____

All About Cells

Read the following information. The words that are in bold print on this page are hidden in the word search below. Complete the word search.

As if they are putting together pieces of a **puzzle**, scientists look at questions about living things and try to objectively discover how these things come together. When the pieces do not seem to fit, they continue to experiment and test their prediction or **hypothesis**. When the pieces do fit together, the scientists suggest a **theory** about the area they are studying. One of these theories is about **cells**, the most basic materials that make up all living things. Cells go through a **cycle** that allows **life** to continue on the planet.

In order to appreciate what is now known about cells, it is important to understand the history of how people have learned about them. Robert Hooke first used the term *cell,* and Antonie van Leeuwenhoek used a simple **microscope** in order to see single-celled organisms. Later, two German science professors, Matthias **Schleiden** (who studied plants) and Theodor **Schwann** (who studied animals) made important discoveries about cells and living things. These discoveries were later established as part of what biologists now call the cell theory.

In 1952, Rosalind **Franklin** used X-rays to photograph **DNA** molecules found within the **nucleus** of a cell. One year later, James **Watson** and Francis **Crick** were able to use Franklin's discoveries to identify the helix structure of DNA.

```
M  C  V  I  R  E  C  G  F  S  Z  U  C  H  O
T  I  F  R  L  K  E  Q  C  U  P  V  A  Y  N
A  C  C  Z  Q  R  L  H  B  E  V  G  T  P  G
C  B  Z  R  N  M  L  D  D  L  F  A  X  O  Y
N  U  V  B  O  E  S  O  T  C  G  R  B  T  Q
P  G  C  H  I  S  Q  T  K  U  N  U  J  H  Z
E  K  J  D  D  C  C  D  H  N  C  A  C  E  Y
S  F  E  W  A  T  S  O  N  E  O  N  N  S  Q
D  N  I  Y  W  J  O  B  P  N  O  D  S  I  N
K  W  G  L  E  Y  B  O  Y  E  A  R  V  S  X
V  B  D  L  C  A  J  P  V  Q  F  W  Y  A  B
C  X  W  R  E  L  C  Y  C  T  W  W  H  O  K
H  N  I  L  K  N  A  R  F  X  F  R  D  C  P
L  C  C  Y  I  Y  W  A  A  K  E  A  M  W  S
K  L  T  B  Y  Y  J  H  S  V  M  U  O  D  B
```

Name _____

Cell Makeup

Match the descriptions below with their terms.

_____ **1.** cell membrane   **a.** a characteristic that can be passed on to offspring

_____ **2.** DNA   **b.** the jelly-like substance found in the cell

_____ **3.** cytoplasm   **c.** one of several tiny structures within a cell

_____ **4.** gene   **d.** a segment of DNA that, among other things, controls specific traits

_____ **5.** chromosome   **e.** the rigid outer layer that protects plant cells

6. trait   **f.** a structure located in the nucleus that contains DNA

_____ **7.** organelle   **g.** the molecule that contains the genetic material of a cell

_____ **8.** cell wall   **h.** a flexible structure that protects and controls what goes in and out of the cell

9. Write a paragraph about the cell theory. Make sure you state each of the three components along with the names of the scientists who made each discovery.

_____

_____

_____

_____

_____

10. Discuss your thoughts about how the complexity of a cell shows that it must be purposefully designed. Include at least four vocabulary words from this chapter.

_____

_____

_____

_____

_____

Name _____

My Plant Cell

1. In the space below, draw a plant cell. Include and label the *cell wall, cell membrane, nucleus, cytoplasm,* and *chromosomes.*

2. Read the following paragraph and fill in the blanks with the correct terms.

The tomato frog has red skin and blue lines above its eyes. The frog gets those

_____ from its parents. Each of these characteristics is controlled by

_____, which are made of _____. These are located in the

nucleus on _____, which the frog also received from

its parents.

3. Write the following terms in order from smallest to largest: *chromosomes, DNA, genes.*

_____

4. Use the terms *DNA, trait, code, pattern,* and *gene* to describe why each organism is unique.

_____

_____

_____

_____

Name _____

Cell Growth

Obtain materials from your teacher and complete the following:

Question: How can we fill up a bag as much as possible with the balloons we have been given?

Hypothesize: As a group, predict an answer to the question.

1. _____

_____

Test It: Plan and record a strategy to test your prediction. You will have five minutes to try your strategy. Record what happens.

2. _____

_____

Analyze and Conclude:

3. Did you fill up the most space of any group in the class? _____

4. Did your strategy work? _____

5. Given the chance to try again, what would you do differently?

_____

_____

6. What would have happened if you had blown up only one balloon to the size of the entire bag? Explain.

_____

_____

7. How do you think this activity applies to cells?

_____

_____

Name _____

Double Up, Split Up

Answer the following.

1. What is the cell cycle?

_____

_____

2. Describe in detail what happens during each of the following stages in the cell cycle.

Interphase _____

_____

Mitosis _____

_____

Cytokinesis _____

_____

3. Draw pictures to represent each of the three stages of the cell cycle. Label each stage. Draw more than one picture to show the events that occur during mitosis.

Name _____

Tissue Types

Read the paragraph below.

The human body contains four basic types of tissue. Muscle tissue, formed from muscle cells, enables every movement you make. It also allows specific organs to expand and contract. Nerve tissue is made of nerve cells, or neurons. It is responsible for sending electrical messages throughout your body so you can do things like see, hear, and think. Epithelial tissue covers and lines the surfaces of your body and organs. Connective tissue connects, supports, and protects the other three kinds of tissue. It also can transport materials.

The following parts of the human body are made of tissue. Use the information from the paragraph above to determine what kind of tissue each part is. Fill in the blank with the correct kind of tissue.

1. The diaphragm that helps you breathe is mostly _____ tissue.

2. Bone is made of _____ tissue.

3. Brain cells are _____ tissue.

4. The inside layer of the stomach consists of _____ tissue.

5. The heart is made mostly of _____ tissue.

6. The reason the bladder can contract is because it is made of _____ tissue.

7. Ligaments and cartilage are _____ tissues.

8. Arteries are able to withstand the enormous pressure of blood pumping through them. This is because they contain _____ tissue.

9. The surfaces of your body and organs are lined with _____ tissue.

10. The joints in your body are possible because of two kinds of tissues. These tissues are _____ and _____.

Bonus: Consider the description of each type of tissue. Now think of what your blood is made of.

What kind of tissue do you think it is? _____

Explain your answer. _____

_____

Name _____

Organizing Body Parts

1. Define the terms below.

cell _____

tissue _____

organ _____

organ system _____

2. Organize the words from the Word Bank into the appropriate category on the chart.

Word Bank			
digestive	nerve	connective	small intestines
lungs	liver	excretory	immune
epithelial	respiratory	nervous	arm muscles
circulatory	kidney	heart	musculoskeletal
colon	brain	bladder	
muscle	stomach	eyes	

tissue	organ	organ system

3.6A
NOTEBOOK

Name _____

Observing Animal Cells

1. Obtain a flat toothpick, slide, cover slip, eyedropper, paper towel, and staining solution from your teacher.
2. Have one student in your group use the flat end of the toothpick to gently scrape the inside lining of his or her cheek.
3. Have another student gently clean the microscope slide and cover slip. Be careful not to leave fibers from the towel or your fingerprints on the slide and cover slip.
4. On the middle of the slide, using the eyedropper, carefully place a tiny drop of staining solution. If too much solution gets on the slide, take the corner of a paper towel and touch the edge of the drop with it to absorb some of the liquid.
5. Stir the toothpick in the solution on the slide to transfer cheek cells onto the slide. Throw away your toothpick. Carefully place a cover slip over the drop of staining solution.
6. Guide the slide under the stage clips and center it below the low objective. Use the coarse adjustment knob to lower the objective, being careful not to let it touch the slide. While looking into the eyepiece, very slowly turn the coarse adjustment knob moving the objective upward until you can clearly see the individual cells.
7. You may need to slightly move the slide around until you see the cheek cells.
8. Look for the cell membrane, nucleus, and cytoplasm. Using a pencil, draw only what you see in the low power circle below.
9. Next, use the high power objective to view the slide in more detail. Look for the same structures as before. Draw only what you see. Label the structures that you observed. Do not allow your label lines to crisscross.

Cheek Cells

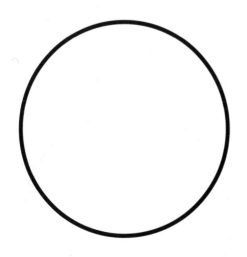

low power

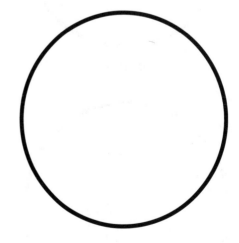

high power

Name _____

Observing Plant Cells

1. Obtain a prepared *Elodea* leaf and an onion skin slide from your teacher.
2. Gently slip the *Elodea* leaf slide under the stage clips so the objective is directly over the leaf.
3. First, use the low power objective to view the slide. Use the coarse adjustment knob to lower the objective. Get it as low as you can without touching the slide. While looking into the eyepiece, very slowly turn the coarse adjustment knob, moving the objective upward until you can clearly see the individual cells.
4. Observe the cells. Look for the cell wall, cell membrane, nucleus, chloroplasts, and cytoplasm. You may not see them all. Using a pencil, draw only what you see in the circles below.
5. Next, use the high power objective to view the slide in more detail. Look for the same structures as before. Draw only what you see. Label the structures that you observed. Do not allow your label lines to crisscross.
6. Repeat Steps 2–5 for the onion skin slide.

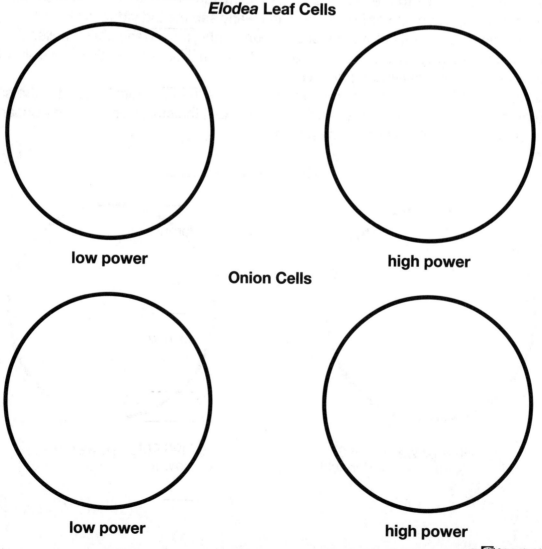

Elodea Leaf Cells

low power

high power

Onion Cells

low power

high power

Name _____

Observing Plant Cells, continued

Based on your observations of *Elodea* leaf and onion cells, complete the following:

1. Describe the shape of the *Elodea* leaf cells.

_____

2. Describe the shape of the onion cells.

_____

3. Why do you think they are shaped that way?

_____

_____

4. Do they share anything in common regarding their shapes?

_____

_____

5. Is there any difference between their shapes?

_____

_____

6. Were you able to see a dark circle inside the cells? If so, what do you think that was?

_____

_____

7. While observing the *Elodea* leaf cells, was there a difference in what you were able to see using low and high power? Explain.

_____

_____

8. While observing the onion cells, was there a difference in what you were able to see using low and high power? Explain.

_____

_____

9. Were you able to see any chloroplasts in either the onion or the *Elodea* leaf cells? If so, describe what you saw and in which kind of cell you saw it.

_____

Name _____

Comparing Animal and Plant Cells

1. Why do you think a staining solution is used for the onion cell and the cheek cell?

_____

2. What color was the *Elodea* leaf, without any stain?

_____

3. Describe the shape of the cheek cells.

_____

_____

4. Why do you think they are shaped that way?

_____

_____

5. Were you able to see a dark circle inside the cells? What do you think that was?

_____

_____

6. How are the cheek cells shaped differently from the *Elodea* leaf cells?

_____

_____

7. How are they shaped differently from the onion cells?

_____

_____

8. Why do you think plant cells were designed differently from animal cells?

_____

_____

9. Why do you think there were no chloroplasts in the onion cells or cheek cells?

_____

_____

Name _____

Common Cancers

Skin cancer is the most common form of cancer. There are two types, melanoma and non-melanoma skin cancers. Melanoma is the most serious type. It starts in the cells that have melanin, the pigment that gives skin its color. Melanoma can develop on any skin surface, and the chance of developing it increases with age. It is more common in lighter-skinned individuals and is rare in people with dark skin.

Non-melanoma skin cancers are much more common and are not as serious as melanoma. They, too, are caused by sunlight exposure. This kind of cancer often forms in skin cells located in the epidermis or on the surface of the skin. Ultraviolet rays penetrate the skin and damage the DNA, causing a mutation. Sometimes the body repairs the damaged cells or the damaged cells just die. However, sometimes the cells try to continue working and duplicate the damaged DNA, which can lead to cancer. The risk of developing all types of skin cancer can be lowered by avoiding overly long periods of sun exposure, wearing hats and clothing to protect yourself, and using sunscreen. Eating foods such as fruits and vegetables that contain antioxidants also may be helpful. Antioxidants, such as vitamins A, C, E and beta-carotene, can protect cells from damage that may lead to cancer.

Lung cancer is another common type of cancer. It forms in the tissues of the lung, especially in the cells that line the air passages. It can spread to other tissues in the chest and to other organs of the body. Scientists have discovered several causes of lung cancer, most of which are related to tobacco use. The best way to lower the risk of lung cancer is to avoid tobacco products. Exercise and diets rich in fruits and vegetables may also lower the risk of lung cancer.

Leukemia is a type of cancer that affects the blood. It begins in blood-forming tissues like bone marrow. Abnormal white blood cells are produced and enter the bloodstream. In time these abnormal cells may crowd out the normal blood cells and cause the blood to not function properly. No one knows the exact cause of leukemia but it seems to develop from either genetic disorders or exposure to high levels of radiation or certain chemicals. Since the exact cause of leukemia is unknown, it is difficult to know how to prevent it.

Colon cancer occurs in the colon, or large intestine. It usually begins as small growths on the intestinal wall called *polyps*. There is no single cause of colon cancer, but there are several factors associated with it. A family history of colon cancer, smoking, heavy alcohol use, physical inactivity, and a high-fat, low-fiber diet can add to the risk of developing this form of cancer. Regular exercise and a diet rich in fruits and vegetables may reduce the risk of colon cancer.

Name _____

Common Cancers, continued

Using the information from the paragraphs on the previous page and what you have learned about organ systems, fill in the blanks on the chart below. Answer the questions.

cancer type	description	system affected	prevention
	DNA mutations in skin cells caused by overexposure to UV rays from the sun	integumentary (skin) system	
	forms in the tissue of the lungs, can spread to other tissues in the chest, often linked to tobacco use		
leukemia			none known at this time
	begins as polyps in the large intestine and is associated with high fat, low-fiber diets		

1. What is the most common type of cancer?

_____

2. Of the cancers described in the paragraphs, which type has the least known about it?

_____

3. Cancer prevention can be different for each different type of cancer. What are two things you can do that seem to help prevent several types of cancer?

_____

_____

4. Why do you think it is important to make good choices about the things you do to your body?_____

_____

_____

_____

Name _____

Vocabulary Review

Write the correct letter of each definition on the blank provided beside each term.

_____ **1.** mutation

_____ **2.** DNA

_____ **3.** cell membrane

_____ **4.** cytoplasm

_____ **5.** organelle

_____ **6.** cell wall

_____ **7.** trait

_____ **8.** gene

_____ **9.** chromosome

_____ **10.** cell cycle

_____ **11.** interphase

_____ **12.** mitosis

_____ **13.** cytokinesis

_____ **14.** cancer

a. a series of events occurring during the life of a cell

b. the stage of cell growth occurring at the beginning of the cell cycle

c. the rigid outer layer that protects and supports plant cells

d. a structure located in the nucleus that contains DNA

e. a change in the DNA sequence of a gene or chromosome

f. a flexible structure that protects and controls what goes in and out of the cells

g. a segment of DNA located on the chromosome that, along with other things, controls specific traits

h. a disease caused by cells that go through uncontrolled cell division

i. the jelly-like substance found inside the cells that contains the organelles

j. a characteristic that can be passed on to an organism's offspring

k. the final stage of the cell cycle in which the cytoplasm divides

l. the stage of the cell cycle in which the cell's nucleus divides in two

m. the molecule that contains the genetic material of a cell

n. one of several tiny structures within a cell

3.8B
NOTEBOOK

Name _____

Chapter 3 Review

Complete the exercises below.

1. List the three parts of the cell theory.

    a. _____

    b. _____

    c. _____

2. Using the terms *DNA, trait, code, pattern,* and *gene*, describe why each organism is unique.

_____

_____

_____

3. List the three main stages of the cell cycle in order.

_____ → _____ → _____

4. Describe two ways in which plant cells differ from animal cells.

    a. _____

    b. _____

5. Explain how cancer forms.

_____

_____

_____

6. How do cells organize into different levels to form an organism?

_____

_____

_____

7. Draw a typical plant cell. Label the *cell wall, cell membrane, nucleus, chromosomes, chloroplasts, DNA, cytoplasm,* and *organelles*.

© *Science* Level 5 • Cells

Name _____

Building Houses

Your group is going to build a graham cracker house. Read and follow the directions exactly as they are worded to complete the activity. Answer the questions.

1. Lay one graham cracker square for the foundation in the middle of the plate. Add the walls by placing four graham cracker sides around the foundation.

Did it work? _____ Did the bottom cracker make a good foundation? _____

2. Remove the graham crackers. Use the plastic knife to spread some frosting in the middle of the plate. Lay one graham cracker square on the frosting, making the foundation. Use more frosting as needed to arrange four graham cracker sides on top of the outside edges of the foundation to make the walls. Allow time to dry.

Did it work? _____ Why do you think so? _____

_____

3. Take two graham cracker squares and make a slanted roof. Did the roof stay up? _____

Why or why not? _____

_____

4. Spread frosting on the edges of the roof supports. Attach two graham cracker squares at an angle to make a pointed roof. Allow time to dry. Did this work? _____

Why or why not? _____

5. Put candy on the roof. Did it stay on? _____ Why or why not? _____

_____

6. Remove any candies in the way. Very gently spread frosting on the roof and on the sides of the house. Decorate it with candies. Did the candies stay on? _____

Why or why not? _____

_____

7. What important concept have you learned from this activity about building a house?

_____

_____

8. What would happen if disaster struck and some of the walls were knocked down?

What would you have to do? _____

_____

Name _____

Interruption Skits

With your group, write the dialogue for a 2–3 min skit. The skit must be about someone trying to give important instructions to a group of people. As the person gives the instructions, the other people in the skit should cause interruptions that make the speaker stop what he or she is saying. The speaker should stop during the interruptions and then return to giving the instructions. There must be as many parts in the skit as there are students in your group. Each person must play a part. Write the dialogue for the skit below. Practice your skit to perform for the class.

_____

_____

_____

_____

_____

_____

_____

_____

_____

_____

_____

_____

_____

_____

1. How did the interruptions interfere with the speaker giving instructions?

_____

2. What did it cause the speaker to have to do?

_____

3. How does this relate to everyday life?

_____

_____

_____

Name _____

Primary Succession Seres

Choose any ecosystem. Describe an ecological interruption in it, which causes primary succession to occur. Draw the four seres of succession in the boxes below as they would normally develop. Include vegetation and animals. Label the *substrate* and *pioneer species*.

1. For the ecosystem you chose, describe the event that causes primary succession

to occur. _____

_____

_____

2. Draw the four seres of primary succession in order.

1.

3.

2.

4.

Name _____

Glacier Bay Plant Succession

Glacier Bay is blanketed with diverse vegetation, from a few pioneer species in newly exposed areas to mature, balanced communities. Since nearly all the vegetation has returned to the land in the last 300 years, this area is one of special interest to scientists. Some of the plants that have colonized Glacier Bay are lichen, moss, dryas, horsetail, fireweed, alder, cottonwood, willow, spruce, and hemlock.

Choose any one of these plants to research. Write an essay about the plant. Include a physical description of the plant, what kind of plant it is, what type of nutrients and climate it needs, and how it reproduces (spores or seeds). If it uses seeds, include whether they are from cones or flowers.

_____

_____

_____

_____

_____

_____

_____

_____

_____

_____

_____

_____

_____

_____

_____

_____

_____

_____

_____

_____

Name _____

Secondary Succession Seres

Pretend you are a pioneer species organism. Write an essay on what you observe as the ecosystem around you becomes reestablished through secondary succession. State what kind of organism you are. Describe the disturbance that initiated the succession and give details about the vegetation and animals that you see. Include the terms *pioneer species*, *seres, softwood*, and *hardwood*.

_____

_____

_____

_____

_____

_____

_____

_____

_____

_____

_____

_____

_____

_____

_____

_____

_____

Name _____

Ants and Succession

Read the following short articles from the *Kansas School Naturalist* and then answer the questions.

ANTS REVEGETATE THE OUTBACK!

Much of our aluminum comes from bauxite mined in Western Australia. These more modern operations were careful to scrape off and store the topsoil before removing the subsoil and extracting the ore. When mining was complete, the subsoil was returned and the rich topsoil was layered on top. Then native grass seed was scattered across the surface and ... nothing grew!

Since they used fresh native grass seed taken from adjacent land, this greatly puzzled scientists. Then they examined what occurred in the unmined grassland. In undisturbed land, any grass seed that lands on the ground was rapidly grabbed by ants and carried underground. On the barren mine topsoil that lacked ants, the seeds "cooked" in minutes. To re-vegetate the Australian bauxite stripmines, they had to add colonies of ants!

ANTS AROUND A PRAIRIE ANTHILL

Western harvester ants accelerate secondary succession in the short grass region of western North America. Seeds gathered by worker ants from surrounding areas are carried into the food storage chambers of the nest where they are eventually eaten or rejected as food. Rejected seeds are carried to the surface and deposited at the edge of the clearing around the cone-shaped gravel and earthen mound. New nests are established in old fields or other disturbed sites adjacent to native vegetation. Seeds carried from the native vegetation may survive to establish native species in the old field around nest sites. Dispersal of progeny from these plants by wind, water, and ants from newly established nests then continues the successional process.

1. Where did the scientists get the seed to replant the area after they had mined? _____

_____

2. Why were the ants important for the succession to occur? _____

_____

3. What type of ant helps disperse seeds in the short grass region of western

North America? _____

4. Where do the ants take the seeds? _____

_____

5. What three factors help continue the succession? _____

_____

Text used by permission from Dr. Thomas Eddy and Dr. John Schrock and is reprinted from Volume 43,1996–97 of the *Kansas School Naturalist.*

Name _____

Determining Succession

Use the Word Bank below to find the term that best describes or completes the following statements. Write your answers on the blanks. One of the terms is used twice.

Word Bank			
primary succession	secondary succession	vegetation	sere(s)
pioneer species	ecological succession	substrate	colonize

1. Sand dunes near the beach cover a large area of land. _____

2. An ecological community will go through a series of changes over time.

_____

3. A factory dumps toxic pollutants into a nearby pond, killing all the animals.

_____

4. The discovery of gold in a mountain community has caused the area to be strip-mined,

leaving it with mostly rocks and no living organisms. _____

5. Mount Vesuvius in Italy erupted, laying down a new layer of _____.

6. As _____ grows back, animals begin to inhabit the

community again.

7. Lichen are commonly the _____ in most ecological

successions.

8. During both primary and secondary succession, each community goes through

several _____.

9. After lichen and moss have broken down the rocks and a sufficient soil base has been

created, larger plants such as ferns and grasses begin to _____

the area.

Name _____

Comparing Successions

Using your vocabulary words and the information you have learned in the chapter about ecological succession, compare and contrast primary and secondary succession. Fill in the Venn diagram below with as many items as you can. Hint: there are at least seven items in each category.

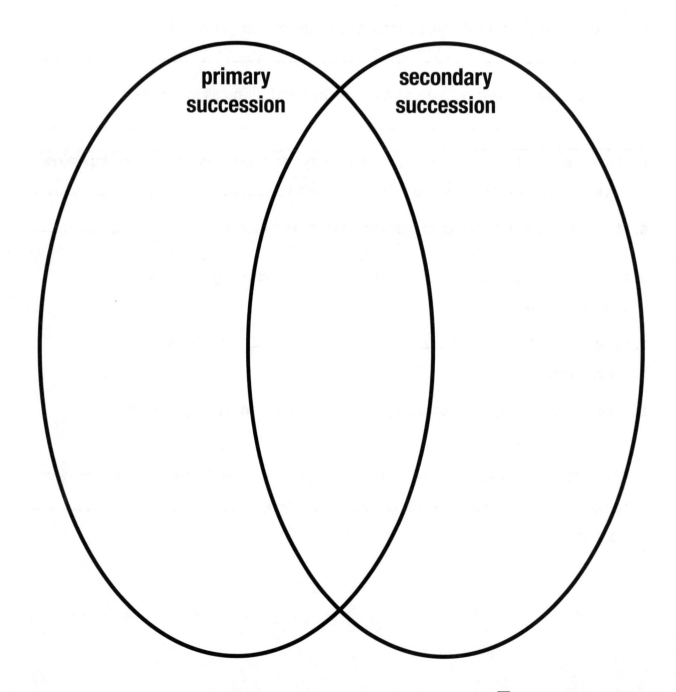

Name _____

Succession Diorama

Use this page to plan your diorama.

My team's topic is _____.

This is an example of _____ succession.

STAGE 1

This sere contains _____.

Team member responsible for this stage is _____.

Ideas _____

_____

STAGE 2

This sere contains _____.

Team member responsible for this stage is _____.

Ideas _____

_____

STAGE 3

This sere contains _____.

Team member responsible for this stage is _____.

Ideas _____

_____

STAGE 4

This sere contains _____.

Team member responsible for this stage is _____.

Ideas _____

_____

Circle the stage you are responsible for completing. The diorama is due on _____.

Please encourage your child, but let him or her do the work to finish the assignment. Please sign and return tomorrow signifying that you understand the directions and how your child is to complete the work.

_____   _____
Student signature   *Parent/Guardian signature*

Name _____

Volcanic Eruption Model

Obtain materials from your teacher. Read through the directions first before beginning the activity. Follow the directions and complete the questions.

1. Lay the paper on the table. Carefully pour the cup of flour on the center of the paper.
2. Have one student in your group position the straw in the middle of the flour pile so the flour buries that end of the straw.
3. While holding the straw in place, have the other students arrange the flour into the shape of a volcano. Use a marker to draw an outline of the base of the volcano.
4. Have one student blow *gently* into the straw. This will create an ash eruption.
5. Using the same color marker as before, outline the extent of the ashfall and identify it with the number *1*. Carefully gather the flour back into the cup.
6. Lay the paper out on the table. Carefully pour the flour onto the exact same spot as before. Follow Steps 2 and 3 but do not mark the volcano position again.
7. Have the same student that blew before do it again. Blow with a little more force this time. Use the other color marker to mark the area of ashfall. Label it with the number *2*.

Complete the following exercises.

1. Explain why the flour was similar to a real ash eruption. _____

_____

_____

2. Which eruption covered a greater area? _____

_____

3. State one reason why you think it was a bigger eruption. _____

_____

_____

4. What other variables could account for the differences in the explosions? Explain why

you think those variables would affect the explosions. _____

_____

_____

_____

_____

Name _____

Oily Bird

Read the following paragraphs carefully and then answer the questions on the next page.

Accidents like the *Exxon Valdez* and Deepwater Horizon make headlines, but there are thousands of small oil spills every year. These small spills often go unreported and unnoticed. However, they can cause damage to the surrounding ecosystems. The oil from these spills comes from motorboats, illegal dumping of old motor oil, street pollution that washes into the sewer systems, and unintentional spills.

Even a small amount of motor oil can be a danger to waterfowl, which are birds that live on or around water. God designed these birds' feathers with a structure that does not allow water or air to penetrate. It helps keep the waterfowl buoyant and warm. Birds spend a lot of time preening, or cleaning and arranging, their feathers each day. This grooming spreads their bodies' natural oil over their feathers.

When motor oil sticks to the feathers, it causes them to separate. This allows cold air and water to penetrate to the skin. The bird preens to get the oil off the feathers, but the oil then gets into its internal organs. This can cause serious damage or death.

Most rescued waterfowl are suffering from either hypothermia (extreme cold) or hyperthermia (overheating) and dehydration. They are frightened, exhausted, and stressed. Rescuers do not wash them immediately. They clean the eyes, mouth, and nasal passages. Then they give the birds fluids and food. When the birds are stable, they go through a series of washes. Rescuers have found that Dawn® dishwashing liquid is the most effective and non-irritating oil remover. An average bird requires two people working approximately 45 min and using 1,136 L (300 gal) of water.

After the waterfowl are thoroughly washed, they are kept warm and allowed to preen themselves. The birds are kept in rehabilitation centers until they are cleared medically, and then released back into the wild. This method can be used on other sea animals, such as otters, and has proven to be effective.

Name _____

Oily Bird, continued

Use the information in the previous passage to complete the following exercises:

1. Name three sources of oil pollution other than tanker spills.

_____

_____

2. Feathers are designed to help the birds stay _____ in the

water and to keep them _____ .

3. What does *preen* mean?

_____

4. What is the difference between hypothermia and hyperthermia?

_____

_____

5. What happens to the birds when they are brought in to be cleaned?

_____

_____

6. How long does it take to wash an average bird?

_____

7. If 270 birds were affected by an oil spill and needed to be cleaned, how many minutes
would it take for two people to clean them all? Show your work.

Minutes _____

How many hours? _____ How many days? _____

Name _____

Vocabulary Review

The vocabulary words on the leaves are answers to the clues below. Match the clue with the vocabulary word and write the number of each clue on the correct leaf.

1. This is a stage in succession.
2. This is the series of events after a disturbance and where soil is still present
3. It bears cones.
4. This is an area's features such as the mountains, valleys, and rivers.
5. Its leaves drop off in the fall.
6. This is the series of predictable changes over time.
7. This is the base that plants and animals live on.
8. This is the assortment of first plants to grow.
9. Barren land begins this series of events.
10. This is what plants do when they grow in an area.
11. Plants are also known as this.
12. This is the study of environmental relationships.
13. Plants are this scientist's favorite thing to study.

Name _____

Chapter 4 Review

Identify the following descriptions. Write the first letter(s) of the correct term in the blank. Choose from the following terms: **(S)** Sere, **(SS)** Secondary Succession, **(PS)** Primary Succession, and **(ES)** Ecological Succession.

_____ **1.** A huge tornado just destroyed an ecological community but left the soil base.

_____ **2.** Pioneer species grow back first.

_____ **3.** A field will naturally go through predictable changes.

_____ **4.** A volcano just erupted, forming a brand new island.

Write complete sentences to complete the following exercises:

5. Give three examples of types of a base for starting a new substrate.

_____

6. Explain how soil is formed in primary succession.

_____

_____

_____

7. Why are glacial retreats so devastating to the land?

_____

8. What types of communities developed during primary succession at Glacier Bay?

_____

9. Explain why fires are not always considered bad.

_____

_____

10. The Mount Saint Helens eruption consisted of ash, volcanic rocks, and some lava. Several areas were protected by the topography, allowing various seeds and roots to survive. Is this primary or secondary succession? Explain your reasoning.

_____

_____

_____

Name _____

Measure the Classroom

Measure the distance between two opposite walls in a classroom. Record your observations below.

1. Place your feet heel to toe and slowly walk from one side of the room to the other in a straight line. Be sure to start with your heel against the wall.

2. Record how many of your foot lengths it takes to walk heel to toe across the room. Use fractions if the distance is not a whole number of foot lengths.

_____

3. Repeat Steps 1 and 2 and record your second measurement below.

_____

4. Explain any differences between your two measurements.

_____

_____

_____

_____

5. Find three classmates and write their answers from Step 3 below.

Classmate 1: _____

Classmate 2: _____

Classmate 3: _____

6. Explain any differences between your measurement in Step 3 and your classmates' measurements. Who has the correct measurement?

_____

_____

_____

_____

_____

Name _____

Find the Right Measurement

In your group, find a way to answer the question below. Record your results and answer the questions.

Question: How can we measure the room so that everyone gets the same answer?

Hypothesize: As a group, discuss the most efficient way to do this. Record your strategy.

_____

_____

Test It:
1. After you have written your strategy, get approval from your teacher to test it out.
2. You will have about 5 min to measure the classroom three times. Record all three measurements and describe what happened below.

Measurement 1: _____

Measurement 2: _____

Measurement 3: _____

_____

_____

Analyze and Conclude:
1. Explain any differences between your measurements.

_____

_____

2. Did your strategy work? _____

3. Given the chance to try again, what would you do differently?

_____

_____

_____

Name _____

Measure and Calculate

Use metric and customary rulers, a meterstick, and a yardstick to make the following measurements and calculations. Give all length measurements in both metric and customary units. Give all area calculations only in metric measurements and show your work. Round to the nearest tenth.

1. the length of your pencil

_____   _____

2. the thickness of the pencil's graphite

_____   _____

3. the span of your hand (with your fingers spread out) from the outside of your thumb to the outside of your little finger

_____   _____

4. your arm span (Spread out your arms against a wall. Have your partner measure from the tip of your longest finger on one hand to the tip of your longest finger on the other hand.)

_____   _____

5. your height

_____   _____

6. the area of your desktop

_____

7. the area of your teacher's desktop

_____

8. the area of your classroom

_____

Name _____

Find the Volume

Get two square pieces of aluminum foil from your teacher. Fold the sides of the foil together to form a box that can hold water. Follow the directions below to complete the activities.

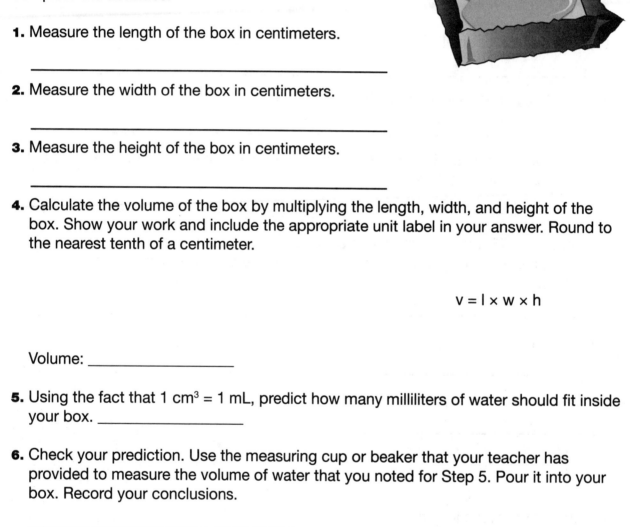

1. Measure the length of the box in centimeters.

_____

2. Measure the width of the box in centimeters.

_____

3. Measure the height of the box in centimeters.

_____

4. Calculate the volume of the box by multiplying the length, width, and height of the box. Show your work and include the appropriate unit label in your answer. Round to the nearest tenth of a centimeter.

$$v = l \times w \times h$$

Volume: _____

5. Using the fact that 1 cm^3 = 1 mL, predict how many milliliters of water should fit inside your box. _____

6. Check your prediction. Use the measuring cup or beaker that your teacher has provided to measure the volume of water that you noted for Step 5. Pour it into your box. Record your conclusions.

_____

_____

_____

_____

_____

Name _____

Measuring Mass and Weight

Use the balance and scales to measure and weigh the items. Record your measurements and complete the exercises.

1. Estimate how much mass you think your science textbook has. Record your estimate in grams or kilograms.

_____

2. Estimate how much you think your science textbook weighs. Record your estimate in ounces or pounds.

_____

3. Use the metric and customary scales to measure the mass and weight of your textbook. Record the measurements using grams or kilograms and ounces or pounds.

mass: _____   weight: _____

4. Estimate and record the mass of a pencil. Use grams as your unit of measurement.

_____

5. Measure the mass of the pencil on the metric scale. Record your measurement.

_____

6. One kilogram can be described as 2.2 lb. Explain how the two units are different and why scientists prefer to use grams and kilograms instead of ounces and pounds.

_____

_____

_____

_____

_____

_____

Name _____

Temperature Tangle

Read the dialogue below. Analyze it and use your textbook to complete the exercises.

Cindi and Maria are friends. Cindi is from the United States and Maria is from Taiwan. One day they decided to go for a walk. It was a lovely summer day and the sun was shining brightly. "It is 26 degrees outside," said Maria. "The weather is perfect for walking!"

"Are you kidding?" asked Cindi, looking out the window. "If it is only 26 degrees, I should wear a coat or I will freeze!" Maria looked confused as Cindi pulled on her coat, hat, and mittens. They opened the door and went outside. "Why, it is so warm out here! It must be almost 80 degrees!" exclaimed Cindi. "I don't need this coat." She took off her coat, hat, and mittens and put them back in the house. The two friends walked a short distance. They began to talk.

"I was sick yesterday," said Maria. "My temperature was 38 degrees. I am so glad to be feeling better today." Cindi stopped and looked at Maria. She was very confused.

"Your temperature was 38 degrees?" Cindi asked. "That sounds like hypothermia to me!" Suddenly both girls stopped and began to laugh. They had just realized why they were so confused.

1. Explain why Maria and Cindi were both confused.

   _____

   _____

   _____

2. Why did Maria say she was sick if her temperature was 38 degrees? What is the average normal body temperature on both scales?

   _____

   _____

   _____

3. If Cindi were to state the boiling and freezing points of water, what would she say? What would Maria say?

   _____

   _____

   _____

Name _____

Density of Water

Follow the directions below to calculate the density of water. Label your measurements and calculations with the appropriate units.

1. Place an empty measuring cup on the scale. Record the cup's mass. _____

2. Take the cup off the scale and fill it with 120 mL of water. What is the volume of

the water?_____

3. Place the measuring cup with water back on the scale. Record its mass. _____

4. Subtract your answer for Step 1 from your answer for Step 3. Record this mass.

_____

5. Explain why it is important to subtract the mass of the empty container from the

overall mass of the container with water. _____

_____

_____

6. Calculate the density of water. Remember, density equals the mass divided by the

volume. (Density = mass ÷ volume) Show your work.

My calculated density of water is _____.

7. Does your answer match what the textbook says about the density of water? Explain

your answer. _____

_____

_____

_____

_____

Name _____

Density of a Solid

Follow the directions below to calculate the density of the object. Label your measurements and calculations with the appropriate units.

1. Fill a measuring cup with 120 mL of water. Record its volume. _____

2. Place the measuring cup with water on the scale. Record its mass. _____

3. Place your object in the water on the scale. Record the new volume and mass.

_____

4. Subtract the volume in Step 1 from the volume in Step 3. Record the object's volume.

_____

5. Subtract the mass in Step 2 from the mass in Step 3. Record the mass of the object.

_____

6. Calculate the density of the object. Remember, density equals mass divided by volume. (Density = mass ÷ volume) Show your work.

My object's density is _____.

7. Is your object more or less dense than water? Give two reasons for your answer.

_____

_____

_____

_____

Name _____

Distance Events

Follow the directions below to complete the events. Record your measurements using the appropriate units and complete the exercises.

Event 1: Shuttle Run

1. Have a partner use a clock or stopwatch to time how long it takes you to run back and forth twice from the starting line to the finish line. Either a foot or hand must touch the line each time. You may repeat the event two more times to get a better time if you wish.

    Record your times: _____ _____ _____ Circle the best one.

2. The shuttle run is 5 m (5.5 yd) in length. How many total meters did you run? (If you repeated the event, include the repetitions in your calculations.)

    _____

3. How long is this distance in yards or feet? (Round the answer.) _____

Event 2: Standing Long Jump

1. Stand behind the starting line with both feet on the ground. Your toes should not touch the tape but be just behind it. Jump as far as you can across the line, making sure to land on both feet in the box marked by tape. The goal is not height but length. Have your partner place a piece of tape at your heel mark closest to the starting line. Measure how far you jumped, both in meters and yards. You may repeat the event two more times to get a better distance if you wish.

    _____ _____ _____ m/cm   _____ _____ _____ yd/in

2. Add the distances you jumped and record the total in both meters and yards.

    _____ m/cm   _____ yd/in

3. Measure the length and width of the box used for the long jump. Calculate and record its area below using an appropriate unit of measurement. Show your work.

    _____

Name _____

Distance Events, continued

Follow the directions below to complete the events. Record your measurements and complete the exercises.

Event 3: Javelin Throw

1. Stand behind the starting line. Your toes should not touch the tape but be just behind it. Load your straw with a cotton swab. Inhale through your nose. Place the straw in your mouth and blow hard and fast. The swab should shoot out. Place a piece of tape at the farthest point where the swab landed. Measure the distance it flew. Repeat the event two more times to get a better distance, but use a clean cotton swab each time.

   Record the distances your swab flew, in both meters and yards:

   _____ _____ _____ m/cm _____ _____ _____ yd/in.

2. Add the distances your swab flew and record the total in both meters and yards.

   _____ m/cm _____ yd/in.

3. Based on your answer in Step 2, calculate how many total centimeters and inches your swab flew.

   _____ cm _____ in.

Event 4: Discus Throw

1. Stand behind the starting line with both feet on the ground. Your toes should not touch the tape but be just behind it. Throw your plate as far as you can across the line. Measure how far your plate flew. Repeat two more times.
   Record your throws in meters and yards:

   _____ _____ _____ m/cm _____ _____ _____ yd/in.

2. Add the distances your plate flew and record the total in both meters and yards.

   _____ m/cm _____ yd/in.

3. Based on the measurement in Step 2, calculate how many total centimeters and inches your plate flew.

   _____ cm _____ in.

4. How could you alter the plate to make it fly farther?

   _____

Name _____

Area and Volume Event

Follow the directions below to complete the event. Record your measurements in appropriate units and complete the exercises.

Event 5: Boat Race

1. Use the supplies you have been given to construct a small sailboat. When your sailboat is completed, place it in the tub next to your partner's. On the count of three, both you and your partner blow your sailboats across the tub of water until they hit the far side. Measure the distance your boat went. This measurement is the length of the tub.

     Record the length: _____

2. Measure the width of the tub.

     Record the width: _____

3. Calculate the surface area of the water and record your calculations using appropriate units. Show your work.

     Area: _____

4. Measure the height of the tub.

     Record the height: _____

5. Calculate the volume of the tub. Show your work.

     Volume: _____

6. Why would you not fill the tub to the top for a boat race?

_____

_____

_____

_____

Name _____

Volume, Mass, and Temperature Event

Olympic competitors get hungry and thirsty! Use the ingredients and measuring tools that your teacher has provided to measure a snack. You must use some of every ingredient. The total volume of your snack must equal 240 mL (1 cup). Record your measurements and complete the exercises.

Event 6: Snack Mix

1. Record the volume measurement for each of the five ingredients. Label them with the appropriate units. Add the measurements to get the total.

    Ingredient 1: _____
    Ingredient 2: _____
    Ingredient 3: _____
    Ingredient 4: _____
    Ingredient 5: _____

    Total Volume: _____

2. Measure the mass of each ingredient using the balance. Record the masses below. Add the measurements to get the total.

    Ingredient 1: _____
    Ingredient 2: _____
    Ingredient 3: _____
    Ingredient 4: _____
    Ingredient 5: _____

    Total Mass: _____

3. Measure the temperature of the water you have been given using both Celsius and Fahrenheit. Record the temperatures below. Label them appropriately.

    _____   _____

4. Add ice and drink mix to your water and stir. Wait a few minutes before taking the temperatures again. Record them below. Label them appropriately.

    _____   _____

Name _____

Sink the Boat

Use the boat you made for **Science Notebook 5.6C Area and Volume Event** to complete the activity. Complete the following exercises.

Question: How many coins will it take to sink your boat?

Hypothesize: Predict the number of coins it will take to sink your boat. Record your hypothesis.

_____

Test It:

After you have written your hypothesis, carefully place coins in your boat, one at a time, until it sinks. Record what happens below.

_____

_____

Analyze and Conclude:

1. Did your boat sink? _____

2. Was your hypothesis correct? _____

3. If a coin is dropped into the water by itself, it sinks. Why do you think it floats if it is dropped into your boat?

_____

_____

_____

_____

Share:

4. Explain why a ship made of steel floats even though steel is more dense than water.

_____

_____

_____

_____

Name _____

Cartesian Divers

Use the materials your teacher provided to design a Cartesian diver and complete the exercises below.

1. Cut your straw in half. Bend the straw in half again. Place a partially unbent paper clip into both ends of the straw. Put a small piece of modeling clay on the bottom of the paper clip. See the illustration for help.

2. Test your diver to see if it has the correct amount of buoyancy. Put the diver in a glass of water. The folded part of the straw should not stick up high above the water line. A small section of the straw can be above the line. Adjust the amount of clay until it barely floats.

3. Fill the bottle with water. Quickly place the Cartesian diver with the clay end facing downward into the bottle of water. Add water to replace any that spills out. Tightly screw on the lid. Squeeze the bottle.

4. Describe what happens.

_____

_____

_____

_____

5. Listen as your teacher explains why this happens. Write the explanation below, using the words *displace*, *fluid*, and *buoyancy* in your explanation.

_____

_____

_____

_____

_____

_____

_____

_____

_____

_____

_____

Name _____

Vocabulary Review

Fill in the blanks with the correct letter of the definition that matches the vocabulary word. Use your textbook as needed.

_____ **1.** buoyant force   _____ **7.** kilo-

_____ **2.** centi-   _____ **8.** mass

_____ **3.** deci-   _____ **9.** milli-

_____ **4.** density   _____ **10.** standard unit

_____ **5.** displace   _____ **11.** volume

_____ **6.** fluid   _____ **12.** weight

a. a measure of the amount of matter of an object

b. a prefix meaning one-thousandth of a unit

c. the measure of how compact matter is, where mass is compared to volume

d. a prefix meaning one-hundredth of a unit

e. a substance that can flow

f. the amount of space matter occupies

g. an upward force in fluids that opposes gravity

h. a prefix meaning one thousand units

i. a measure of the pull of gravity on an object

j. a prefix meaning one-tenth of a unit

k. to push aside

l. an established quantity used for measure and comparison

Name _____

Chapter 5 Review

Length

Fill in the charts below with the correct amounts and units. On the blank beside each row, write the property that the units in that row are used to measure.

metric units	property
10 millimeters (mm) = 1 centimeter (cm)	_____
_____ (mg) = 1 gram (g)	_____
_____ (mL) = 1 liter (L)	_____
1,000 meters (m) = _____ (km)	length
_____ (cm) = 1 meter (m)	_____

customary units	property
_____ (in.) = 1 foot (ft)	_____
_____ (oz) = 1 pound (lb)	_____
1,728 cubic inches (in.³) = 1 cubic foot (ft³)	_____
_____ (ft) = 1 mile (mi)	_____
_____ (ft) = 1 yard (yd)	_____

Temperature

Circle the correct temperature for each description.

1. normal human body temperature   212°F   98.6°F   32°C
2. boiling point of water   212°C   32°F   100°C
3. normal human body temperature   100°F   37°C   37°F
4. freezing point of water   0°F   98.6°C   32°F
5. freezing point of water   0°C   0°F   100°F
6. boiling point of water   212°F   98.6°F   100°F

Name _____

Chapter 5 Review, continued

Area and Volume

Find the area of the rectangle and the volume of the rectangular prism. Show your work. Provide the units of measurement in your answer.

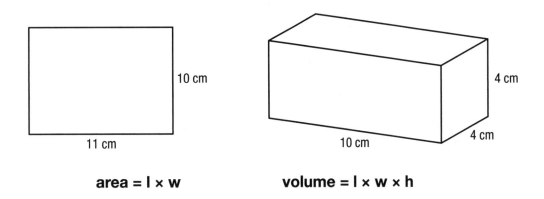

area = l × w   **volume = l × w × h**

Area: _____ cm²   Volume: _____ cm³

Complete the following exercises. Show any necessary work.

1. The volume of a rectangular prism is 1,000 cm³. Rewrite the volume in mL and L.

_____

2. A book weighs 2.2 lb and has a mass of 1 kg. What would happen to these quantities if the book were sent to the surface of the moon?

_____

_____

3. Imagine that the perimeter of the block where you live is 2,000 ft around. If you walked around it twice, how many inches would you have walked? Show your work.

_____

Name _____

Chapter 5 Review, continued

Volume and Density
Complete the following exercises. For calculations, show your work.

1. A rock has a volume of 30 cm³ and a mass of 300 g. What is its density? How does it compare to the density of water?

Density: _____

$$\text{Density} = \frac{\text{mass}}{\text{volume}}$$

_____

2. Explain in a paragraph why steel ships can float on water even though steel is more dense than water.

_____

_____

_____

_____

Units of Measurement
Read and analyze the following paragraph. Answer the questions.

Thumbelina is the name of the world's smallest horse. Thumbelina is a dwarf miniature chestnut mare. She stands only 44.5 cm or 17 $\frac{1}{2}$ in. high. While an average horse can have a mass of 454 kg or weigh 1,000 lb, Thumbelina has a mass of 25.85 kg, weighing only 57 lb.

1. Give an example of a country where people would measure Thumbelina's attributes using the customary system.

_____

2. Give an example of a country where people would measure Thumbelina's attributes using the metric system.

_____

3. How do you know that Thumbelina is unique? What would happen if you did not have standard units to measure her with?

_____

_____

Name _____

Watchful Eye

Imagine you are a crime scene investigator. The person who walked into your classroom a few minutes ago is a witness to a crime. You need to question him or her but no one knows who he or she is. Your job is to describe this individual as best you can so he or she can be found.

1. Write down as many descriptive details as you possibly can.

_____

_____

2. How well did you pay attention to the person who walked into the room? Do you feel that you described the individual well enough for someone else to find him or her?

_____

3. Find three other students and compare your descriptions with each other. Did they list

any details that you omitted? What were they? _____

Did you list any details that they did not? _____

How hard is it to describe someone in detail? _____

🛑 **STOP HERE: Wait for your teacher's instructions before completing Exercises 4-7.**

4. That same person just walked into the room again. Here is another chance to observe him or her more carefully. Without talking, write down as many characteristics about the visitor as you can.

_____

_____

5. Was your first description or your second one more complete? Why?

_____

6. Why do you think it might be important to pay attention to what is happening around

you? _____

_____

7. Explain why it is important for scientists to make detailed observations.

_____

_____

_____

Name _____

Handle a Candle

Begin by observing a candle and listing its properties. Your teacher will then perform a demonstration. Observe him or her carefully. Complete the exercises after each phase of the demonstration.

1. Observe the physical properties of the candle. Record four of your observations.

   a. _____   c. _____

   b. _____   d. _____

2. Observe the candle after your teacher lights it. Record three different observations.

   a. _____   c. _____

   b. _____

3. Watch closely for at least 20 seconds while your teacher demonstrates holding a

   copper coil in the flame of the candle. Describe what happens. _____

   _____

   What happens when your teacher moves the copper coil up and down in the flame

   _____

4. Describe the results after your teacher holds the glass lid over the flame.

   _____

5. Watch the candle and the glass jar after your teacher puts the ice cube on top of the jar and places it over the candle. List two observations.

   a. _____   b. _____

6. Based on your observations, identify three products from the burning candle.

   a. _____ b. _____ c. _____

7. Compare the properties of these products to the candle.

   _____

   _____

8. Have you observed any of these outcomes before? Write about your experience. Include what happened and what the circumstances were that caused it to occur.

   _____

   _____

   _____

Name _____

Mixture Madness

Obtain materials from your teacher. Follow the directions below to make and then separate a mixture. Complete the exercises.

1. Keep the samples of salt and sand apart. Observe them carefully and record three physical properties of each one.

Sand: **a.** _____ **b.** _____ **c.** _____

Salt: **a.** _____ **b.** _____ **c.** _____

2. Pour the sand and the salt into the bowl and mix them together. Observe carefully.

Do the sand and the salt appear to be evenly distributed throughout? _____

Is this mixture a solution? _____

3. Use the stir stick to try and separate the sand from the salt. Is this easy or hard?

_____

Would it take a long time to separate it in this way? _____

4. Plan another way to separate the sand and the salt. Record your plan.

_____

_____

5. Have your teacher approve your method. Gather the necessary materials to test your plan. Try out your idea and record the results.

_____

_____

6. Did your plan work?_____ If not, think of another method and record it. Get approval from your teacher and gather any materials you may need. Keep trying until you find a plan that works.

_____

_____

7. Did your method of separation cause any physical changes? _____ Explain why your method worked and include any physical changes you may have used.

_____

_____

_____

Name _____

Solubility

Follow the directions and complete the exercises.

1. At the ends of two paper towel strips, make a large circle with the permanent black marker. Label the other ends of the strips—one with the letter *A* and the other with the letter *C*. At the end of the third paper towel strip, write the letter *B*. On the opposite end make a large circle with the watercolor marker. Set aside the towel strip labeled *C*.

2. Pick up the strip labeled *A*. Dip the circle end into the cup of water just enough so that the water touches the edge of the paper and begins to spread through the black circle. Describe what happens.

_____

3. Is the ink on strip *A* soluble in water? _____ Is water a solvent for the

permanent ink on strip *A*? _____

4. Write a sentence using the words *permanent ink*, *insoluble*, and *water* to describe

what you have just observed. _____

_____

5. Pick up the strip labeled *B*. Dip the circle end into the cup of water just enough so that the water touches the edge of the paper and begins to spread through the black circle. Describe what happens.

_____

_____

6. Is the ink on strip *B* soluble in water? _____ Is water a solvent for the

watercolor ink on strip *B*? _____

7. Look at strip *B* again. Write a sentence using the term *mixture* to describe the

watercolor ink. _____

_____

8. Pick up the strip labeled *C*. Dip the circle end into the cup of alcohol just enough so that the alcohol touches the edge of the paper and begins to spread through the black circle. Describe what happens.

_____

9. Is the ink on strip *C* soluble in alcohol? _____ Is alcohol a solvent for

the permanent ink on strip *C*? _____

© Science Level 5 • Changing Matter

Name _____

Changing Matter

Watch your teacher perform an experiment that will demonstrate a chemical change. Then complete the exercises.

1. Record your observations of the steel wool after your teacher flattens it.

_____

2. Your teacher will place the steel wool in a bowl and add enough white vinegar to completely cover the steel wool. Record your observations of the white vinegar.

_____

3. This combination must be left alone for about 10 min. Watch as your teacher then removes the steel wool and places it in a clear, empty plastic bottle. Describe any changes in the steel wool. Your teacher will discard the vinegar.

_____

4. Your teacher will now cover the top of the bottle with a deflated balloon to create what is called a *closed system*. No substance can enter or exit the system. Your teacher will use a scale or a balance to measure the mass of the closed system.

   a. Record the mass in grams. _____

   b. Sketch a diagram of the closed system on a separate piece of paper.

5. After the sealed bottle sits for 24 hours, make and record your observations.

_____

6. Your teacher will measure the mass of the entire system.

   a. Record the mass in grams. _____

   b. Make another sketch of the closed system on your extra piece of paper.

7. Describe what happened to the mass of the closed system before and after.

_____

8. Your teacher will remove the balloon and extract the steel wool from the bottle. Record

   your observations. _____

9. What evidences of a chemical change did you observe? Give three examples.

   a. _____

   b. _____

   c. _____

6.4B
NOTEBOOK

Name _____

Mix It Up

Record your observations during the demonstrations led by your teacher. Complete the exercises.

Disappearing Act
One glass container is half full of water. The second container is half full of bleach. Watch as your teacher dips one cotton swab in food coloring and then stirs the water in the first container. Watch again as your teacher dips the second cotton swab in food coloring and then stirs the bleach in the second container.

1. Describe how the liquid in the first container changed.

_____

2. Describe how the liquid in the second container changed.

_____

3. Continue to watch the second container of bleach. After 3 min, compare the two containers and describe your observations.

_____

_____

4. What type of change occurred in the second container? What is the evidence?

_____

_____

Gooey Sweetness
Your teacher will place a solid chocolate bar on a piece of waxed paper near a heat source until it becomes warm. He or she will then allow it to cool.

1. Observe and record what happens. _____

2. Describe what happened after the chocolate cooled down. _____

_____

3. Observe the chocolate after it has hardened. Record your observations. _____

_____

4. What type of change took place? _____

5. Compare the melted chocolate bar with the original. Why do you think the bar looks different than the original?

_____

© *Science* Level 5 • Changing Matter

Name _____

Chain Reactions

Nuclear fission begins when a neutron moving at a very high speed hits and splits the nucleus of another atom. This is also called *splitting the atom*. When this happens several additional neutrons are released from the nucleus as it breaks apart. These additional neutrons may each collide with other atoms and split other nuclei. This process, or chain reaction, continues to repeat itself, causing large amounts of energy to be released. Follow the directions for *Methods 1* and *2* in the activity below. Complete the exercises.

Method 1:
a. On a smooth, flat surface, stand one domino on its short side.

b. Arrange the rest of the dominoes in such a way that when one domino falls, it only strikes the next domino. Use **BLM 6.5A Dominoes** for help if needed.

c. Use a stopwatch to time how long it takes for all the dominoes to fall. Be ready to start and stop the stopwatch quickly. Push over the first domino so that it falls onto the next domino. Record the time. Describe what happened.

_____

_____

Method 2:
a. Move the dominoes to the side. Stand one domino on its short side. Arrange two more dominoes so that when the first domino is pushed over, it will knock over the next two.

b. Continue placing two dominoes behind each single domino so that each domino will strike two other dominoes when it falls. Use BLM 6.5A for help setting up the dominoes. You may need to repeat setting up the dominoes a few times to get all the dominoes to fall correctly.

c. Once the dominoes have been correctly arranged, time *Method 2* using the stopwatch. Record the time. Describe what happened.

_____

_____

_____

1. Did *Method 1* or *2* take less time for all the dominoes to fall? _____

2. Which method was louder as it fell? _____

3. Which method produced more energy in a shorter amount of time? _____

4. Which method best modeled nuclear fission? _____

5. Explain your reasoning for your answer to Exercise 4. _____

_____

Name _____

Nuclear Fission: Advantages and Disadvantages

Read the following paragraphs and complete the exercises.

Nuclear fission produces about 13–15% of the world's electricity, but almost 75–80% of France's electricity. The fuel for fission is the element uranium. The amount of energy available through nuclear fission is millions of times greater than the amount available through chemical changes like burning fuels. Therefore, the amount of uranium needed is much less than the amount of other fuels, such as coal, oil, or natural gas. This makes nuclear power the source of energy often chosen for submarines that stay under water for months at a time. As well, the fissioning of uranium does not release smoke or carbon dioxide gas into the air as the burning of other fossil fuels does.

However, there are concerns about the use of nuclear power. Fission produces waste that releases large amounts of radiation. Storage of these waste products is expensive. Many residents prefer not to have a nuclear plant built nearby or to have radioactive waste stored in their neighborhoods. Accidents at a nuclear power plant can harm many people, animals, and the environment. Two major nuclear disasters, at Chernobyl, Russia in 1986 and at Fukushima, Japan in 2011, caused much damage. These disasters brought many changes to nuclear power plants and resulted in several countries reducing or eliminating nuclear power plants. Although there are problems with nuclear energy, the benefits of providing electricity to the world usually outweigh the negative aspects.

1. Underline the facts in the article.
2. Circle the reasoned judgment or possible result.
3. Draw a box around the opinion or preference.
4. List two advantages of nuclear fission as a source of energy.

a. _____

b. _____

5. List two disadvantages of nuclear fission as a source of energy.

a. _____

b. _____

6. Explain your opinion on whether or not nuclear power should be used as an energy source where you live. Include reasons for your opinion.

_____

_____

Name _____

Marshmallow Models

Follow the directions to construct models of water
molecules (H_2O) and to illustrate three types of changes.

1. Into the side of one large marshmallow, insert one toothpick tilting diagonally upward.
Insert a second toothpick at the same angle on the opposite side of the marshmallow.
Attach one small marshmallow on each tip of the toothpicks. This represents one
molecule of water (H_2O). Make three more models in the same manner.

2. Line up the four marshmallow models end to end. Remove the small marshmallows
from the toothpicks, except for the one on the outer left-hand and outer right-hand
sides. Connect the models with tissue paper by pushing the tissue paper onto the
toothpicks. One piece of tissue paper should connect two models. Put the small
marshmallows back on the toothpicks. This now represents a model of solid ice.

3. a. What do the toothpicks represent? _____

b. What does the tissue paper represent? _____

c. What do the small marshmallows represent? _____

d. What do the large marshmallows represent? _____

4. Describe how your model can show a physical change. Which bonds would need to
be broken?

_____

_____

5. Separate the four marshmallow models from each other. This is now a model of liquid
water. Demonstrate the chemical change of breaking down water into hydrogen and
oxygen atoms. Describe what you did to your model and which chemical bonds
were broken.

_____

_____

6. This is now a model of the elements hydrogen and oxygen. Demonstrate nuclear
fission with the oxygen atom. Describe what you did and which bond was broken.

_____

_____

7. Which type of bond or force is the strongest? _____

8. Which bond or force is the weakest? _____

Name _____

Soluble or Insoluble

Follow the directions to demonstrate solubility and insolubility.

1. Obtain a 350 mL (12 oz) glass containing 60 mL ($\frac{1}{4}$ cup) of honey.
2. Slightly tip the glass and pour 60 mL ($\frac{1}{4}$ cup) of liquid dish soap down the side of the glass and onto the honey.
3. Add two drops of food coloring to 60 mL ($\frac{1}{4}$ cup) of water and stir. Very slowly add the colored water to the mixture by pouring it down the side of the tipped glass.
4. Add 60 mL ($\frac{1}{4}$ cup) of vegetable oil to the mixture in the same way.
5. Add two drops of a different food coloring to 60 mL ($\frac{1}{4}$ cup) of rubbing alcohol and stir. Add this to the mixture very carefully in the same way.
6. Record your observations. Include a sketch of what you observe. Label each layer with the substance's name.

_____

_____

_____

_____

_____

7. List the substances in order from least dense to most dense.

_____

_____

8. Is food coloring soluble or insoluble in rubbing alcohol? _____

9. Is vegetable oil soluble or insoluble in rubbing alcohol? _____

10. Is liquid dish soap soluble or insoluble in honey? _____

11. How can you test whether rubbing alcohol is soluble or insoluble in water? _____

_____

12. Test your idea. Describe the results. _____

_____

13. Is rubbing alcohol soluble or insoluble in water? _____

14. Stir the entire mixture. Wait for it to settle. Describe what happens and explain why.

_____

_____

Name _____

Fizzing Fun

After making your prediction below, read through all the directions before getting started. Always point the canister lid away from yourself and others. Take turns keeping time and holding the canisters. Obtain materials from your teacher and listen for additional directions. Complete the following exercises.

Question: How can I speed up the reaction time so that the lid pops off faster?

Hypothesize:

_____

_____

Test It:

1. Take the lids off and fill five film canisters half full with water.

2. Prepare to place a whole effervescent tablet in one of the canisters. The timer should use a stopwatch to begin timing as soon as you drop in the tablet. Drop the tablet into the canister and be ready to quickly snap the lid on tightly. Hold the canister straight up in your hand so that your fingers do not touch the lid. Stretch out your arm away from your body. Be careful not to point the canister toward anyone. Measure the amount of time it takes for the lid to pop off the canister. Record the time in the *Data Table* found on **Science Notebook 6.6D Fizzing Fun Results**.

3. Predict the time it will take for the lid to come off after using only half an effervescent tablet. Write your prediction: _____Test your prediction by repeating the method in Step 2. Record the time in the *Data Table*.

4. Now predict how much time it will take for the lid to come off after using a tablet that is broken into 10 pieces. Prediction: _____ Test your prediction and record the time in the *Data Table*.

5. On a sheet of paper and with a spoon, crush the tablet into a powder before adding it to the water. Predict how much time it will take for the lid to come off after adding the powder. Prediction: _____ Test and record this time in the *Data Table*.

6. For the fifth film canister, break the tablet up in yet another way to produce a different time than the other trials. Predict how much time it will take for the lid to come off using your method. Prediction: _____Describe your method: _____

_____

7. Test your method to see if your prediction is correct. Record the time in the *Data Table*.

Name _____

Fizzing Fun Results

Fill in the results from the experiment on **Science Notebook 6.6C Fizzing Fun** in the *Data Table*. Draw a line graph of the results and complete the exercises.

Analyze and Conclude:

Data Table	
trial	**time in seconds**

Title: _____

label: _____

label: _____

1. Which canister had the fastest reaction time? _____ the slowest? _____

2. What variable caused the difference in the reaction times?_____

_____

3. What type of change did you perform on the tablets before they were placed in

the water? _____

4. What type of change happened inside the canister? _____

How do you know? _____

5. Based on what you observed, write two conclusions about chemical changes.

a. _____

_____

b. _____

_____

6. Did your predictions get more accurate with each new trial? _____

7. Why do you think that happened? _____

_____

Name _____

Combustion

Use the terms *exhaust*, *heat*, *fuel*, and *oxygen* to fill in the diagram illustrating the process of combustion. Hint: Heat is used twice. Complete the remaining exercises.

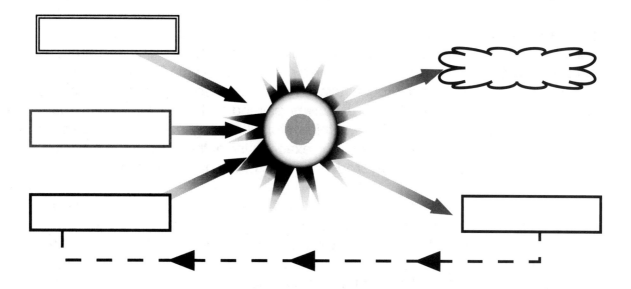

1. What are the three components needed for combustion to occur?

_____

2. In the above diagram, what are the two products of the combustion reaction?

_____

3. What property of hydrogen makes it useful as a fuel?

_____

4. Name another combustible element or compound mentioned in this chapter.

_____

5. Besides hydrogen, give two other substances that are used for fuel.

_____

6. Compare and contrast a car engine to a space shuttle engine.

_____

_____

_____

Name _____

The Hindenburg

In 1936 air travel between Germany and the United States began in the *Hindenburg*, an airship powered by hydrogen. The *Hindenburg* made 10 round trips that carried a total of 1,002 passengers. On May 6, 1937, the *Hindenburg* made its final cross-Atlantic trip. While landing at Lakehurst, NJ, the enormous airship burst into flames. Most accounts say it completely burned in less than a minute. That day, the *Hindenburg* carried 97 people, of which 36 died. An early investigation concluded that hydrogen leaked, caught fire, and caused the disaster. Hydrogen is highly combustible and lighter than air, which makes it buoyant. The ship contained several chambers that held hydrogen, allowing the vessel to float. The frame of the blimp-shaped ship was covered in a canvas painted with a reflective aluminum coating that was combustible. The lightning storm that night could have created static electricity that produced a spark. The exact cause of the fire is still in question, but the US government banned hydrogen airships following the tragedy.

Almost 100 years after the *Hindenburg* tragedy, hydrogen travel is returning as a possibility. Today, hydrogen is being tested and used as fuel for hydrogen fuel cell cars. Researchers hope that hydrogen will become a cheaper and cleaner fuel for the cars of the future. People are concerned about driving a car that has a highly combustible fuel. Another danger of a hydrogen fueled car is an electrical shock from the high voltage needed to power the electric motor. The amount of electricity is about three times as much found in a regular car. Governments want to increase the number of cars that use cleaner fuel than gasoline. Public safety is a concern that auto makers must address in the design and testing of the vehicles. However, like the *Hindenburg* tragedy, hydrogen car disasters could end the future of hydrogen cars. Scientists continue to experiment with other alternatives to hydrogen that are less combustible.

1. What might have caused the fire that burned the *Hindenburg*?

_____

2. What effect did the *Hindenburg* have on hydrogen fueled airships?

_____

3. What is appealing about hydrogen cars?

_____

4. What are two dangers of hydrogen cars?

_____

5. Would you drive a hydrogen fueled car? Explain why or why not based on the article.

_____

Name _____

Vocabulary Review

Write on the line in the correct box the number of the vocabulary word that fits the description. If you have matched them correctly, the sums of each row and each column will be the same number. Not every vocabulary word will be used.

1. chemical property   **5.** physical change   **9.** soluble

2. nuclear change   **6.** physical property   **10.** chemical bond

3. insoluble   **7.** solution   **11.** substance

4. mixture   **8.** chemical change   **12.** combustibility

alters the form or size, not the type of matter _____	the ability to burn _____	occurs in the nucleus of an atom, results in new elements _____	SUM _____
a single kind of matter that is pure _____	describes when or how a substance interacts with other substances _____	two or more substances that are evenly distributed _____	SUM _____
unable to be dissolved in a given substance _____	characteristic of a substance which can be observed or measured _____	the force of attraction that holds atoms together _____	SUM _____
SUM _____	SUM _____	SUM _____	

Name _____

Chapter 6 Review

Use the following terms as many times as needed to correctly complete the statements.

Word Bank	physical change	chemical change	nuclear change
	physical property	chemical property	

1. A _____ _____ forms different elements.

2. Breaking the bonds between molecules is a _____ _____.

3. Combustibility is a _____ _____ because it describes how a substance will react with another substance.

4. Melting, freezing, and dissolving are each a _____ _____.

5. Atoms get rearranged during a _____ _____.

6. _____ _____ describes when or how a substance will interact with other substances.

7. A _____ _____ only changes the form or size of matter.

8. A _____ _____ forms new substances with different properties without changing the individual atoms.

9. A _____ _____ alters the nucleus.

10. _____ _____ describes the size or appearance of a substance or mixture.

Pictured here is a glass of rocks and sugar water. Use the picture and the terms in the Word Bank to complete the statements.

Word Bank	mixture	insoluble	solution	soluble

11. The mixture of sugar and water is called a _____ because it is evenly distributed and appears the same throughout.

12. The rocks and the sugar water are called a _____ because the different parts can be physically separated.

13. Sugar is _____ in water.

14. Rocks are _____ in water.

Name _____

Making It Easier

Do you ever wonder why and how often you use tools? Circulate through all five stations with your group. Wait for your teacher to instruct you to move to a station. Read and perform each activity and then answer the questions. Do not use tools or any object other than your hands.

Question: What advantages do tools give you?

Hypothesize: Record why you think people use tools.

_____

_____

Test It:

Station 1

1. Try to open the paint can by taking off the lid. How hard is it to do without any tools?

_____

2. What would you use to make this job easier?

_____

Station 2

1. Try to pull the nail out of the wood. Are you able to do it without help from any objects?

_____

2. What tools would you choose to make this job easier? _____

_____

Station 3

1. Try to open the can without any tools. Are you able to do it? _____

2. What tools would you suggest to help you open the can?

_____

3. Try to crack open the nutshell to get the nut out. Remember, you cannot use anything but your hands. Is this easy or hard to do?_____

4. What tools and other objects would you suggest to open the nutshell?

_____

Name _____

Making It Easier, continued

Station 4

1. Cut the log into six pieces. Can this be done without an object to help you?

_____

2. What tools would you use to get this job done?

_____

3. Try inserting the screw all the way into the wood. How easy is this task?

_____

4. What tools would make this easier? _____

Station 5

1. Divide the piece of paper into two halves. The edges must be sharp and clean cut without any frayed pieces of paper. Remember, do this with only your hands. Were you able to divide the paper into two halves?

_____

2. Do the halves have clean, sharp edges?

_____

3. What tools would you use to get sharper edges?

_____

Analyze and Conclude:

1. Now that you have performed these activities, why do you think tools are used instead of hands alone? _____

_____

_____

2. Is your answer now different than your prediction? Explain. _____

_____

_____

3. Write one statement about something you have learned from these activities.

_____

_____

Name _____

Magnets and Force

mass	×	acceleration	=	force
m	×	a	=	f

The mass of a falling rock accelerates at a given rate to hit the ground with a certain amount of force. Use the information below to calculate the force.

1. 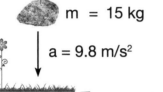 m = 15 kg

a = 9.8 m/s²

f = ? ← (ground)

Solve for force (f).

_____ x _____ = _____ newtons

2. 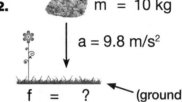 m = 10 kg

a = 9.8 m/s²

f = ? ← (ground)

Solve for force (f).

_____ x _____ = _____ newtons

3. If the mass is greater and the acceleration is the same, then the _____

will be greater. If the _____ is less, the force will be less at the same acceleration.

Watch your teacher perform a demonstration. Then complete the following exercises.

4. What caused the force that moved the steel ball that your teacher placed into

the trough? _____

5. Describe the motion and acceleration of that steel ball.

_____

_____

6. How did that steel ball cause the steel ball at the other end to move?

_____

_____

7. Would low-strength magnets be able to create the same effect? Explain.

_____

_____

Name _____

Work, Work, Work

Obtain materials from your teacher for this activity. During the activity, complete the following exercises. The formulas for force and work are provided in the box below.

1. Make a chute by placing one end of the tube on top of a stack of books and the other end on the floor.

2. Hold the golf ball at the top of the chute.

3. Drop the ball, allowing only the force of gravity to move it.

4. Repeat using the Ping-Pong ball.

$$\text{force} = \text{mass} \times \text{acceleration}$$
$$\text{work} = \text{force} \times \text{distance}$$

5. Measure and record the distance each ball rolled before coming to a stop.

    golf ball: _____ cm   Ping-Pong ball: _____ cm

6. Measure and record the mass of each ball. golf ball: _____ g

    Ping-Pong ball: _____ g

7. A force was applied to each ball due to the force of _____.

8. _____ occurs when a force moves an object in the same direction as the force.

9. A _____ is the unit used to measure work.

10. Which ball rolled farther? Why?_____

    _____

11. Predict what will happen when you drop the balls through the tube with a wooden

    block at the end. _____

12. Place a wooden block at the end of the chute. One at a time, drop each ball through

    the chute. Describe what happens. _____

    _____

13. What work took place? _____

14. Did you correctly predict the results? What caused this result?

    _____

    _____

Name _____

Identifying Types of Simple Machines

Look at the pictures. Use the Word Bank to label each type of simple machine.

| **Word Bank** | lever | wheel and axle | inclined plane | wedge | screw | pulley |

1. _____

4. _____

2. _____

5. _____

3. _____

6. _____

List examples of some simple machines that are used at home.

7. lever

_____

_____

_____

8. wedge

_____

_____

_____

9. wheel and axle

_____

_____

_____

10. screw

_____

_____

_____

11. inclined plane

_____

_____

_____

12. pulley

_____

_____

_____

Name _____

Describing Simple Machines

1. How does a lever work?

_____

_____

2. Describe how an inclined plane can make work easier.

_____

_____

3. A bicycle is a compound machine made of simple machines. Draw a line to each type of simple machine and label—*lever, wheel and axle*, and *screw*. Find at least one example of each of the three different simple machines.

Name _____

Identifying Classes of Levers

Study each illustration and circle the name of the class of lever represented. The triangle with the letter *F* represents the fulcrum.

1. First-class   Second-class   Third-class

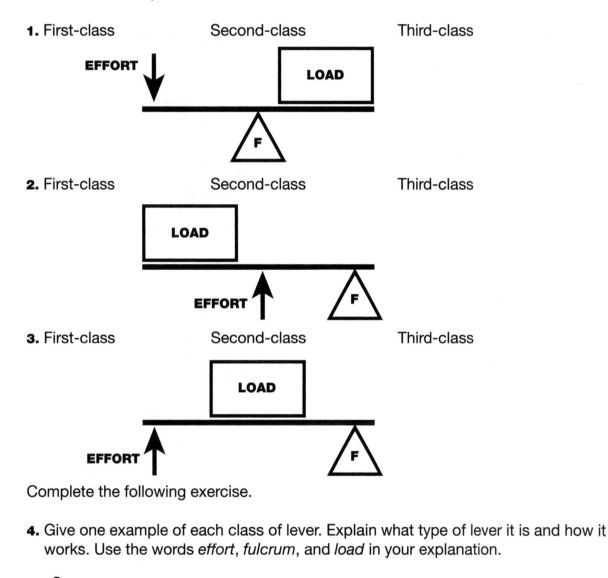

2. First-class   Second-class   Third-class

3. First-class   Second-class   Third-class

Complete the following exercise.

4. Give one example of each class of lever. Explain what type of lever it is and how it works. Use the words *effort*, *fulcrum*, and *load* in your explanation.

   a. _____

   _____

   b. _____

   _____

   c. _____

   _____

Name _____

Effort and Load

Read the class of lever for each illustration; then on the illustrations, mark an *E* to identify the effort, an *L* to identify the load, and an *F* to identify the fulcrum. Draw an example for Exercise 7.

1. Third-class lever

2. Third-class lever

3. Third-class lever

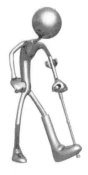

4. Second-class lever

5. Second-class lever

6. First-class lever

7. First-class lever

Name _____

Force and Distance in a Lever

First-class levers are common and vary in shape and size. The effort and the load are not always the same distance from the fulcrum. The arrangement changes the amount of effort it takes to lift a load. Follow the directions below to build your lever system so that the load is lifted as high as it can go.

1. On your piece of card stock, use a ruler to draw two parallel lines that are 5 cm (2 in.) from the left and right sides. You should now see three rectangles.

2. Fold the two sides along the lines you have just made to form a 3-D triangle. Tape the open edges together at the top. This will be your triangular fulcrum.

3. Take a small piece of paper and make a label that reads *Load*. Tape the label to the film canister and then tape the canister to the meterstick at the middle of the 5 cm measurement. This is where your load will stay.

4. Make another label *Effort* and tape it to the other canister. Wrap a piece of tape loosely around the opposite end of the meterstick with the sticky side out. Place the second canister on top of this piece of tape. The *Effort* canister should now be able to slide along the meterstick. Slide the canister and place it over the 95 cm mark.

5. Place the 50 cm mark of the meterstick on one point of the triangular fulcrum.

6. Place three pennies in the *Load* canister.

7. Predict how many pennies the *Effort* canister will need to lift the load all the way up.

_____

8. Count the pennies as you drop them into the *Effort* canister one at a time until the load is lifted completely. Look at the chart on **Science Notebook 7.6B Lever Data Chart**. Find the *Effort Force* column and fill in the number of pennies it took to lift the load with the *Effort* canister located at 95 cm. Compare your prediction to the actual number of pennies it took to lift the load.

_____

_____

9. Repeat Step 8 with the middle of the *Effort* canister at 90 cm, 80 cm, 70 cm, and 60 cm. The meterstick may move slightly during this process. Make sure to adjust the meterstick back to the 50 cm mark each time. If this is not done, it will cause inaccurate results. Record the distance from the *Effort* canister to the fulcrum and the number of pennies it takes to lift the load on the *Lever Data Chart*.

Name _____

Lever Data Chart

Answer the questions below based on the data you have already placed in the chart.

Lever Data Chart

effort canister location (cm)	distance between fulcrum and effort canister (cm)	effort force (number of pennies needed to lift the load)
95	45	
90		
80		
70		
60		

1. How many pennies are in the *Load* canister? _____ Compare the amount of pennies in the *Load* cup to the number of pennies in the *Effort* canister for each distance. Write one statement about the comparison between the two.

_____

2. When you moved the *Effort* canister location, what happened to the distance between the fulcrum and the *Effort* canister?

_____

3. Use a ruler to measure the maximum distance that the *Load* canister raises above the tabletop. Record that distance. _____ Did the load move the same distance each time you changed the location of the *Effort* canister and added pennies? _____

4. Because the load lifts up the same distance each time, the same amount of work is being done. What else had to change when the distance between the fulcrum and the *Effort* canister changed?

_____

5. Describe the relationship between the location of the *Effort* canister and the number of pennies (effort force) needed to raise the load.

_____

_____

_____

Name _____

Graphing Results

1. Transfer the data from your chart onto the following graph. Plot the *distance between fulcrum and effort canister* values on the horizontal axis and the number of pennies on the vertical axis. Determine the increments and label each axis with the appropriate numbers.

Effort Versus Distance

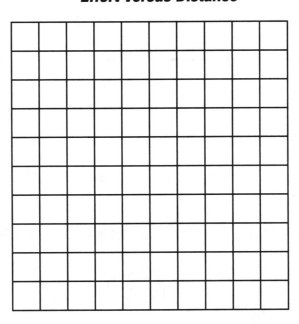

number of pennies (coins)

distance between fulcrum and Effort canister (cm)

2. Describe what you see on the graph. Include the terms *number of pennies* and *distance between fulcrum and Effort canister* in your answer.

_____

_____

_____

3. Do the results of the graph support the statement you wrote in Exercise 5 on the previous notebook page? Explain why or why not.

_____

_____

_____

Name _____

More Levers

Using your previous setup, move the fulcrum so that it is under the *Load* canister with the three pennies in it. Move the sliding canister to the 30 cm mark and place the rest of your pennies in it. Hold the lever at the 95 cm mark and lift it up. Have everyone in the group do this to feel the weight.

1. What class of lever is this? _____

2. Mark the diagram with an *E* to identify the effort, an *L* to identify the load, and an *F* to identify the fulcrum.

3. Notice that the former load is balanced on the fulcrum and its effect is cancelled.

Now move the sliding canister to the 95 cm mark and leave the pennies in it. While holding the fixed canister on the fulcrum, carefully lift the meterstick at the 30 cm mark. Have everyone in the group do the same.

4. What class of lever is this? _____

5. Name the lever class that required more effort to lift the load. _____

6. The advantage of the second-class lever is lifting more weight with less effort. The third-class lever requires more effort to lift a lighter load. This is not an advantage, but this lever helps you in another way. What is the advantage of the third-class lever?

_____

_____

Name _____

Calculating Grade

The angle of an inclined plane determines the grade of the slope. To find the grade, divide the height of the ramp, called the *rise,* by the total length of the ramp, called the *run*. Then convert the fraction into a percentage. This is the grade.

grade = $\dfrac{\text{rise}}{\text{run}}$

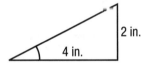

5 in.   1 in.

1. What is the rise? _____ What is the run? _____

   Convert the fraction into a percentage to find the grade. _____

   Use a protractor to measure the angle of the incline. _____

Follow the same procedure as above to complete the exercises.

2 in.
4 in.

2. Rise = _____   Run = _____

   Grade = _____   Angle of Incline = _____

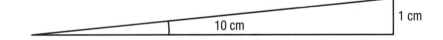

10 cm   1 cm

3. Rise = _____   Run = _____

   Grade = _____   Angle of Incline = _____

4. Compare the grades from above to their angles of incline.

   Does the largest grade come from the largest angle of incline? _____

   Does the smallest grade come from the smallest angle of incline? _____

   How would you describe the relationship between a grade and its angle of incline?

   _____

   _____

Name _____

Archytas and Archimedes

Read the following paragraphs and answer the questions. Underline all of the possible answers that you find in each paragraph.

Archytas (400–350 BC) lived at the same time as Plato, who was his friend. Archytas was a Greek mathematician, scientist, philosopher, statesman (politician), and military leader. He was the first to apply mathematics to mechanics and is credited with inventing the screw, the pulley, and the baby rattle. Archytas made numerous mathematical achievements in astronomy and the theory of music.

Archimedes (287–212 BC) was also a Greek mathematician as well as physicist and engineer. He is not only credited with discovering the principle of buoyancy, now known as *the Archimedes principle*, but he also designed many machines that were far ahead of their time. Archimedes explained how the lever works, which became the basis for understanding the science of mechanics. He demonstrated mathematically that there is a ratio between the effort applied to raise the load and the distances of the effort and the load to the fulcrum. Archimedes developed a system of compound pulleys that was used to pull ships. He also designed the Archimedes screw, a device used to raise and remove water from the bottom of ships.

1. Who is credited for inventing the screw and pulley? _____

2. List three positions or jobs that Archytas held.

_____

3. Use a dictionary to look up the word *mechanics*. Write the scientific definition.

_____

4. Write two of the achievements of Archimedes that are discussed in the paragraph.

_____

_____

5. Archimedes' principle of the lever demonstrates a ratio between what two things?

a. _____

b. _____

6. What did you observe to be true when you did the lever activities in the previous lesson? Explain.

_____

_____

Name _____

Vocabulary Review

Fill in the blanks with the correct vocabulary term to complete the sentences.

1. The _____ is a pivot point on which a lever rotates.

2. The train's _____ is 60 kph in an easterly direction.

3. Moving an object in the same direction as the applied force is

   _____.

4. It takes _____ to do work.

5. A change in an object's velocity is considered _____.

6. A ramp is a(n) _____.

7. _____ are used to measure force.

0. _____ are used to measure work.

9. The force applied to a simple machine is the _____.

10. Walking up a slope with a 60% _____ would be

    very difficult.

11. The measure of how fast an object moves in a given amount of time is the

    _____.

12. _____ are devices used to make tasks easier.

13. The _____ has three different classes.

14. The object moved when an effort is applied is the _____.

15. Draw an example of each of the three classes of levers. Label the fulcrum, effort,
    and load.

First-Class Lever	Second-Class Lever	Third-Class Lever

Name _____

Chapter 7 Review

In Exercises 1–3, mark each line with an *L* for load, *E* for effort, and *F* for fulcrum. Fill in the circle in front of the correct answer for each of the following.

1. The load is between the fulcrum and the effort.

⎯⎯⎯⎯⎯⎯⎯⎯⎯⎯

○ first-class lever   ○ second-class lever   ○ third-class lever

2. The effort is between the fulcrum and the load.

⎯⎯⎯⎯⎯⎯⎯⎯⎯⎯

○ first-class lever   ○ second-class lever   ○ third-class lever

3. The fulcrum is between the load and the effort.

⎯⎯⎯⎯⎯⎯⎯⎯⎯⎯

○ first-class lever   ○ second-class lever   ○ third-class lever

4. Suppose that you have a heavy load of books to take to the classroom next door. Which tool would work best for a heavy load that needs to move a short distance?

○ first-class lever   ○ second-class lever   ○ third-class lever

5. Suppose that you played baseball and scored a home run by hitting the baseball into the outfield. Which tool was used for the moving the ball a long distance?

○ first-class lever   ○ second-class lever   ○ third-class lever

6. The speed of a bicycle traveling 91 miles in 7 hours is ___. $speed = \dfrac{distance}{time}$

○ 637 mph   ○ 13 kph   ○ 637 kph   ○ 13 mph

7. The grade of a slope with a rise of 1 and a run of 5 is ___. $grade = \dfrac{rise}{run}$

○ 20%   ○ 25%   ○ 50%   ○ 15%

8. Identify the type of simple machines below. Use the following letters: L = lever, W = wedge, WA = wheel and axle, IP = inclined plane, S = screw, P = pulley

_____ garage door   _____ door handle   _____ wheelbarrow

_____ crowbar   _____ mini blinds   _____ bicycle gears

_____ ax   _____ knife   _____ wheelchair ramp

Name _____

Rewrite the Story

Read the story from **BLM 8.1A Mitchell's Morning**. Read the two sentences below and use the information in them to rewrite the story. Give it a new title.

Mitchell awoke in complete darkness to the sound of his mother's voice calling, "Mitchell, get up! The storm last night knocked out the electrical energy in our house!"

New Title _____

_____

_____

_____

_____

_____

_____

_____

_____

_____

_____

_____

_____

_____

_____

_____

_____

_____

_____

_____

_____

Name _____

Analyze the Story

Use the story from **BLM 8.1A Mitchell's Morning** and the story you rewrote to complete the exercises below.

1. List at least 10 items mentioned in *Mitchell's Morning* that require electrical energy.

_____   _____

_____   _____

_____   _____

_____   _____

_____   _____

2. Write each item listed in Exercise 1 in the appropriate column based on its source of power. If an item uses both as possible sources, place it in the *battery* column.

power company	battery

3. Of the items you listed above, which ones have a substitute that does not require electricity? Describe the function of each item and its substitute.

_____

_____

_____

4. Look around your classroom, identify two items that use electrical energy, and describe how your school day would be different without each of them.

a. _____

_____

b. _____

_____

Name _____

Current

Use the materials you have been given to complete the activity. Follow the directions carefully in order to avoid injury. Complete the exercises.

1. In your group decide on one person to hold the wire and another to hold the battery. Set the battery on its side on a hard surface. The person selected to hold the battery should hold the middle of the battery so that it does not roll. Avoid touching the ends.

2. The person selected to hold the wire should hold it with two fingers near each end. His or her fingers should be on the plastic covering about 1 cm ($\frac{1}{2}$ in.) from the exposed end of the wire. Be careful not to touch the wire until you are told to do so.

3. The person with the wire should place one exposed copper end of the wire against each end of the battery. Try to center the ends of the wire in the middle of each end of the battery. Hold the connection and slowly count to 15.

4. Take the wire away from the battery. Quickly and carefully feel the ends of the wire.

5. Repeat 1–4, rotating members of your team so that everyone has a chance to try the experiment.

6. Describe what happened to the wire after connecting the ends of the battery. Why did this happen? What would happen if the wire were only connected to one end of the battery?

   _____

   _____

   _____

7. Examine the wire you were given. What are its components? Why are these specific ones used?

   _____

   _____

8. Why was it necessary to remove small sections of plastic from both ends of the wire in order to conduct the experiment?

   _____

   _____

9. How are static discharge and current electricity similar? How are they different?

   _____

   _____

   _____

8.3B
NOTEBOOK

Name _____

Voltage

Examine the picture below. Complete the exercises.

1. In a brief paragraph, describe how this picture relates to voltage.

_____
_____
_____
_____

2. Draw a picture, different from the one above, that illustrates voltage. Describe it below.

```




```

_____
_____
_____
_____

© Science Level 5 • Electricity and Magnetism

Name _____

Series Circuits

Follow the directions on **BLM 8.4B Instructions: Circuits**. Complete the exercises.

1. Construct a series circuit with one lightbulb. Draw it in the space below.

2. Place the battery in the battery holder. Describe what happens.

_____

3. Construct a series circuit with two lightbulbs. Draw it in the space below.

4. Describe if the lightbulbs are brighter, dimmer, or the same as they were in Step 2. Explain why.

_____

_____

_____

5. Unscrew one bulb while the battery is in its holder. Describe what happens to the second bulb. Explain why you think it happened.

_____

_____

_____

6. Circle the correct word or phrase to make each statement true:

As a series circuit gets longer, resistance ___.

      increases   decreases   stays the same

As a series circuit gets longer, the amount of current available ___.

      increases   decreases   stays the same

Name _____

Parallel Circuits

Construct each circuit according to the directions on **BLM 8.4B Instructions: Circuits**.
Complete the exercises below.

1. Construct a parallel circuit with two lightbulbs. Draw it in the space below.

2. Plug in the battery. Describe what happens.

_____

3. Construct a parallel circuit with three lightbulbs. Draw it in the space below.

4. Describe if the lightbulbs are brighter, dimmer, or the same as they were in Step 2.
Explain why.

_____

_____

_____

_____

5. Unscrew one of the lightbulbs. Describe what happens and at least two ways that
series and parallel circuits are different.

_____

_____

_____

_____

Name _____

Attract and Repel

Follow the directions below to complete the activities and draw the magnetic fields.

1. Place two magnets end to end with about 3 cm (1 in.) between them. Make sure their opposite poles are facing each other.

2. Place cardboard on top of the magnets and center it over them. Place a sheet of white paper over the cardboard. Sprinkle iron filings carefully and sparingly over the surface of the paper.

3. Tap the surface of the paper lightly to concentrate the iron filings on the lines of magnetic force. Draw what you see below.

4. Carefully pick up the white paper, keeping it flat so that the iron filings do not slide off. Roll it carefully into a funnel and pour the filings back into their container.

5. Rearrange the two magnets so that they are end to end with about 3 cm (1 in.) between them. Make sure the southern poles are facing each other.

6. Now repeat Steps 2 and 3. Draw what you see below.

7. What does this activity demonstrate?

_____

_____

_____

Name _____

Related Forces

Follow the steps below to complete the
activity. Then complete the exercises.

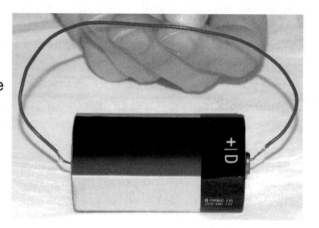

1. Use the piece of electrical tape to attach
   one end of the copper wire to the negative
   end of the battery. Make sure the wire is
   centered on the battery's end.

2. Touch the loose end of the copper wire to
   the positive end of the battery. Make sure
   to handle only the insulated portion of the
   wire since the exposed copper may get
   very hot.

3. While both ends of the battery are connected, have your partner carefully hold the wire
   over the top of the compass. He or she should move the compass in a circle under the
   wire and above the battery as you both watch the compass needle.

4. Disconnect the loose end of the wire from the positive end of the battery. Have your
   partner hold the wire over the compass again and move it in a circle.

5. What effect did the wire have on the compass when both ends were connected to
   the battery?

   _____

   _____

6. What effect did the wire have on the compass when both ends were not connected to
   the battery?

   _____

   _____

7. Explain your observations.

   _____

   _____

   _____

   _____

Name _____

Flash in the Pan

Follow the directions below to complete the activity and exercises.

1. Take your pie pan, piece of paper, and tape and lay them on a flat surface. Tape one end of the paper to the middle of the pan. Make a loop with the paper and tape the other end so that the loop stays up. This will be a handle you can use to lift the pan without touching its metal sides.

2. Lay the foam plate upside down next to the pie pan. Make sure the pie pan and foam plate are not touching.

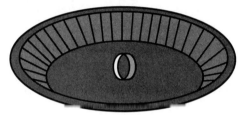 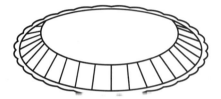

3. Have your partner watch the clock. When he or she says, "Start," carefully begin rubbing the back of the foam plate hard and fast with your piece of wool. When one minute has passed, your partner should say, "Stop." Put the wool aside.

4. Without touching the metal, lift the pie pan by the handle and set it on top of the foam plate. Now touch the tip of one finger to the bottom of the pan.

5. What happened when you touched the metal pan? What is this evidence of?

_____

6. Pick up the pan by the handle. What happens to the plate?

_____

7. Explain this experiment using the following vocabulary words: *charge, static electricity,* and *static discharge*.

_____

_____

_____

_____

_____

_____

Name _____

Make an Electromagnet

Follow the directions and complete the exercises below to construct and compare two electromagnets.

Question: How does the length of a circuit affect an electromagnet?

Hypothesize: As a group, discuss possible answers to the question. Record your prediction.

_____

_____

_____

Test It: Follow the directions below to make two different electromagnets.

1. Find the middle of your shorter piece of insulated wire. Beginning in the middle of the wire and at the middle of the nail, tightly coil the wire around the nail toward both ends. Leave at least 7–8 cm (about 3 in.) of the wire hanging loose from each end.

2. Connect the end of the wires to the battery holder. Make sure the wire remains in a tight coil around the nail.

3. Insert the battery in the battery holder. Your electromagnet should look similar to the one below.

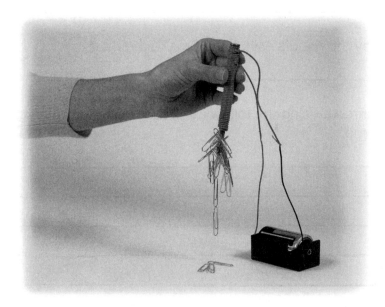

Name _____

Make an Electromagnet, continued

4. Use the nail to try to pick up some of the paper clips. Try it three times and count how many paper clips the nail picks up each time. Record the quantities below.

Trial 1: _____ Trial 2: _____ Trial 3: _____

5. Disconnect the battery. Immediately use the nail to try to pick up some of the paper clips. Keep trying for several seconds. Describe what happens.

_____

_____

_____

_____

6. Remove the wire from the nail and set the wire aside. Find the middle of the longer insulated wire. Beginning in the middle of the wire and in the middle of the nail, tightly coil the wire around the nail toward both ends. Leave at least 7–8 cm (about 3 in.) of the wire hanging loose from each end.

7. Connect the end of the wires to the battery holder. Make sure the wire remains in a tight coil around the nail.

8. Insert the battery into the battery holder.

9. Use the nail to try to pick up some of the paper clips. Try it three times and count how many paper clips the nail picks up each time. Record the quantities below.

Trial 1: _____ Trial 2: _____ Trial 3: _____

10. Disconnect the battery. Immediately use the nail to try to pick up some of the paper clips. Keep trying for several seconds. Describe what happens and how it compares to Step 5.

_____

_____

_____

_____

_____

_____

Name _____

Make an Electromagnet, continued

Analyze and Conclude:

Use the information from your experiment to complete the following exercises.

1. Explain how the nail became magnetic.

_____

_____

_____

2. Explain the difference between the two electromagnets you constructed. How does the length of the wire affect the magnet and why?

_____

_____

_____

_____

3. How is the electromagnet's ability to attract the paper clips affected after the battery is disconnected? Explain your answer.

_____

_____

_____

4. What other factors might influence the strength of an electromagnet?

_____

_____

_____

5. What describes the relationship between current electricity and magnetism? Give two examples of how electromagnets are used today.

_____

_____

_____

_____

Name _____

Identify the Change

Examine each picture. On the lines provided, identify how energy is being changed from one form into another.

Name _____

Choose Energy

Choose and circle two sources of energy that are transformed into electrical energy. In the spaces provided list some advantages and disadvantages of each source. Compare the two and describe which one you would choose to use if you were building a power plant.

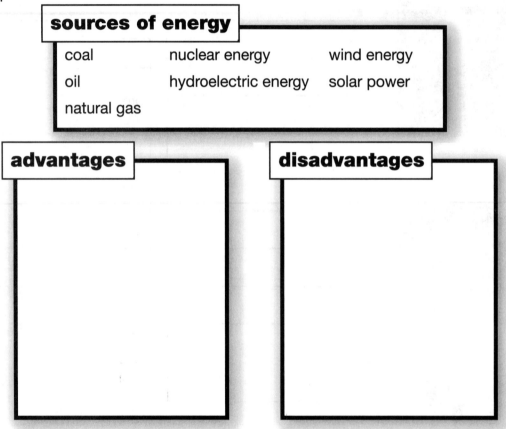

sources of energy

coal	nuclear energy	wind energy
oil	hydroelectric energy	solar power
natural gas		

advantages

disadvantages

1. Describe how the two sources you chose are similar and how they are different.

_____

_____

_____

2. If you were building a power plant to produce electrical energy, what source of energy would you choose and why?

_____

_____

_____

Name _____

Vocabulary Review

The vocabulary words below are not all matched to the correct definitions. Use the labels you have been given to correct the mismatched words and definitions. Remember that many but not all the definitions are wrong!

charge	**circuit**	**current electricity**
a complete path through which an electric current can flow	relating to matter with strong magnetic properties	a machine that produces electricity from moving parts

electromagnet	**ferromagnetic**	**generator**
a magnet that produces a magnetic field by means of an electric current	the power of an electric current, measured in volts	a circuit with more than one path for an electric current

parallel circuit	**resistance**	**series circuit**
the continuous flow of an electric charge through a material	the buildup of nonflowing electric charge	a circuit with a single path for an electric current

static discharge	**static electricity**	**voltage**
a measure of how difficult it is for current electricity to flow	the property of a particle that causes it to attract or repel other particles	a sudden flow of static electricity from one object to another

Name _____

Chapter 8 Review

Complete the exercises below.

1. Look at the atoms below. On the lines provided write *positive* if the atom has a positive charge, *negative* if the atom has a negative charge, and *neutral* if the atom has no overall charge.

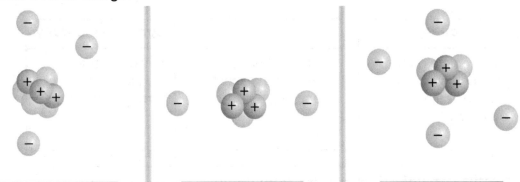

_____   _____   _____

2. Describe the difference between static electricity and static discharge.

_____

_____

_____

3. Draw a parallel circuit with one battery and two lightbulbs below.

4. Does your drawing show static electricity or current electricity? Explain your answer.

_____

_____

5. Explain what would happen if you removed one bulb from a parallel circuit. How is this different than what would happen if you removed a bulb from a series circuit?

_____

_____

_____

Name _____

Chapter 8 Review, continued

Complete the exercises below.

6. Draw two circuits, one with greater resistance than the other. Explain which one has greater resistance and why.

_____

_____

_____

7. Describe what kind of material you would use to construct a circuit and why.

_____

_____

_____

8. If someone asked you to prove that electricity and magnetism were related, how would you do it?

_____

_____

_____

9. List three elements that are ferromagnetic.

_____   _____   _____

10. Describe how an electromagnet works and include at least two factors that affect its strength.

_____

_____

_____

8.8D
NOTEBOOK

Name _____

Chapter 8 Review, continued

Complete the essays below.

11. Explain how your life would be different if you lived before the widespread use of electrical energy.

_____

_____

_____

_____

_____

_____

_____

_____

_____

_____

_____

_____

_____

12. Describe two methods used to generate electricity. Give at least one advantage and one disadvantage of each. Choose one method and state why you prefer it.

_____

_____

_____

_____

_____

_____

_____

_____

_____

Name _____

Predictable Changes

Change is a fact of life. People look different as they grow older. Plants experience several stages as they go through their life cycle. Caterpillars transform into butterflies. Complete the following exercises on this topic.

1. How would the world be different if life were always the same?

_____

_____

_____

2. What is a major change that you have experienced?

_____

3. Name one predictable transformation that usually occurs in school.

_____

_____

_____

4. Predict a change that you expect to happen in your life before you graduate from high school.

_____

_____

_____

5. Write one thing that the Bible says will not stay the same.

_____

6. Give an example of a type of change that is unpredictable.

_____

_____

7. Do you usually like each day to be different? Why or why not?

_____

_____

_____

Name _____

Physical Versus Chemical Changes

Living organisms are not the only things that experience change. So does inorganic or nonliving matter. Sometimes things just look different on the outside. Their physical properties, such as size or shape, may vary, but they are still the same substances. These are physical changes. An example would be cutting a piece of bread in half or dissolving hot cocoa mix in water. Physical changes also involve states of matter, such as when liquid water turns into solid ice. In geology a physical change happens when something breaks apart or moves around but is still the same substance.

However, when things experience a change in their composition, it is called *a chemical change*. One form of matter transforms into another. During this transformation, atoms within the matter's molecules rearrange and form other molecules with different properties. Unlike a physical change, a chemical one cannot usually be reversed, such as a match burning or a leaf changing color in autumn.

Read each description of a change and circle the correct type of change.

1. Two rocks grind together and split apart. **physical**   **chemical**

2. Water erodes pieces of a rock and carries them downstream. **physical chemical**

3. Acid precipitation dissolves limestone and makes a deposit in a cave underground.
physical   **chemical**

4. All of the topsoil from a farmer's field is blown by the wind to one end of the field.
physical   **chemical**

5. Two areas of mud get pushed together by moving water and leave behind a small hill.
physical   **chemical**

6. When a certain type of acid is added to a rock, tiny gas bubbles can be seen where the rock and the acid react. **physical**   **chemical**

7. Draw an example of physical change or chemical change. Explain your picture.

Name _____

Labeling the Plates

1. Label these major lithospheric plates by referring to the Word Bank, looking at the image your teacher displays, or by using an encyclopedia or the Internet.

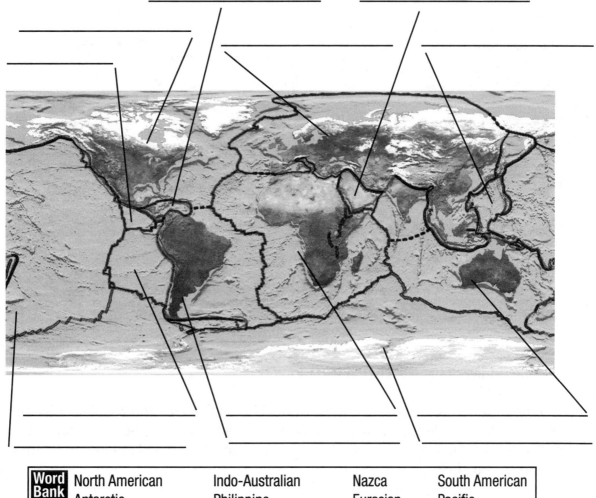

Word Bank	North American	Indo-Australian	Nazca	South American
	Antarctic	Philippine	Eurasian	Pacific
	Caribbean	Cocos	African	Arabian

2. Name and summarize the theory that helped lead to the plate tectonics theory.

_____

_____

_____

Name _____

Plate Movement

Part of the area around the edges of the Pacific Plate is known as *the Ring of Fire*. This area has many active volcanoes and earthquakes, primarily because it is on an active plate boundary. Use the Internet or other resources to complete the exercises below.

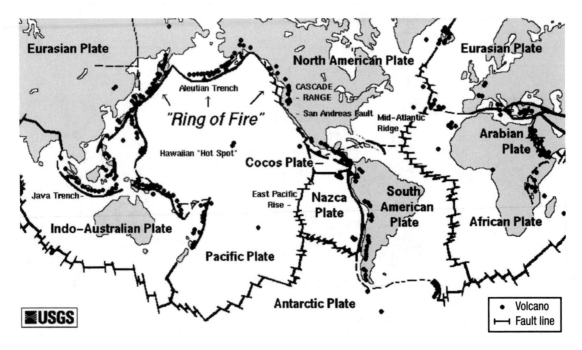

1. Color the edges of the Pacific Plate in red.

2. Some notable volcanoes have erupted in the United States (Mount Saint Helens), the Philippines (Mount Pinatubo), Japan (Mount Fuji), and Mexico (the Paricutin Volcano). Choose one of these and research its specific location. Plot its location on the map by drawing a blue circle.

3. Name one interesting fact you learned about the volcano that you researched.

_____

4. What types of boundaries can cause earthquakes or volcanoes? Explain your answer.

_____

_____

_____

5. Which layers of the earth are divided into plates that move, according to the plate tectonics theory?

_____

Name _____

Graphing the Ocean Floor

Use the information from the table below to make a profile of the ocean floor. To make a profile, plot the data points. Connect them with a ruler to create a line graph. Shade in the area below your line to identify the ocean floor. Give your graph a title and complete the exercises below.

Graph Title: _____

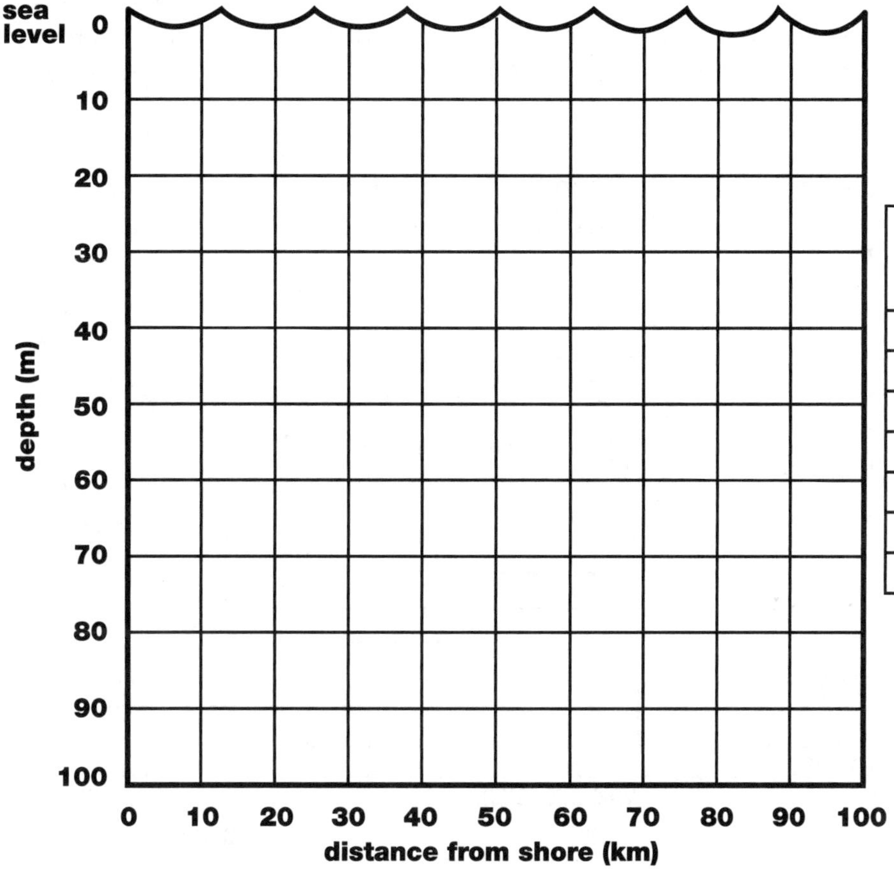

distance from shore (km)	depth (m)
0	0
10	10
25	70
50	85
65	60
80	30
100	50

(Graph grid: y-axis "depth (m)" from sea level 0 at top to 100 at bottom in increments of 10; x-axis "distance from shore (km)" from 0 to 100 in increments of 10.)

1. What does the area between the line you drew and the top of the graph represent?

_____

2. At what distance from shore is the deepest point of this ocean profile? _____

3. Between what distances from shore is the steepest slope shown? _____

4. According to the chart, which ocean feature is most likely located at 80 km from the

shore, a trench or a seamount? _____

5. What ocean feature would begin at 0 km from shore and 0 meters deep?

_____

Name _____

Labeling the Ocean Floor

Read the following paragraph and complete the exercises.

While the continents are located above sea level, the continental margins are the underwater transition areas that slope outward and downward to the rest of the sea. Some areas, like the abyssal plains, are nearly flat portions of the ocean floor. Seamounts, on the other hand, are underwater mountains formed by deposited sediments or layers of lava. If they keep growing, they can become volcanic islands that rise above sea level. On a divergent boundary, an ocean ridge can exist, often with a trench as a very low point between the ridges. These and other features make the ocean an exciting place to explore!

1. Label the following diagram using the words in the Word Bank. Write the correct answer on the lines provided. Some of the words may be used more than once.

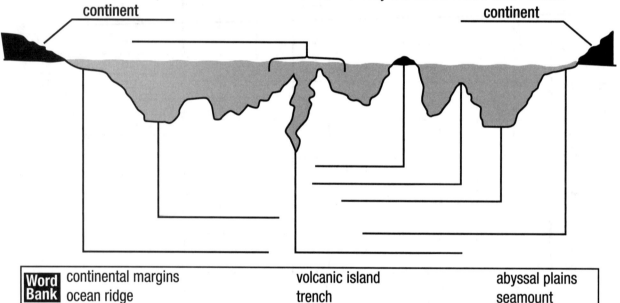

| **Word Bank** | continental margins | volcanic island | abyssal plains |
| | ocean ridge | trench | seamount |

2. Explain how new ocean floor forms.

_____

_____

_____

3. Explain how sonar works.

_____

_____

_____

Name _____

Ice Cube Test

Follow the directions to test the ice cubes that your teacher gives you.

Question: How will temperature and salinity affect the ice cubes?

Hypothesize and Test It:

1. What do you think will happen when the red ice cube is placed into the beaker?

_____

2. Place the red ice cube carefully into the beaker. What happened?

_____

3. What do you think will happen when the blue ice cube is placed into the beaker?

_____

4. Place the blue ice cube carefully into the beaker. What happened?

_____

5. Draw the beaker with colors labelled immediately after adding the ice cubes.

6. Draw the beaker with colors labelled after 5 minutes.

Analyze and Conclude:

7. What do you know about the deep ocean floor that might explain what happened to the red ice cube?

_____

8. What do you know about the surface water that might explain what happened to the blue ice cube?

_____

9. What will happen after the ice cubes completely melt? Explain why.

_____

_____

Name _____

Worldwide Currents

1. Match the currents in the Word Bank to the letters on the map. Then complete the exercises that follow.

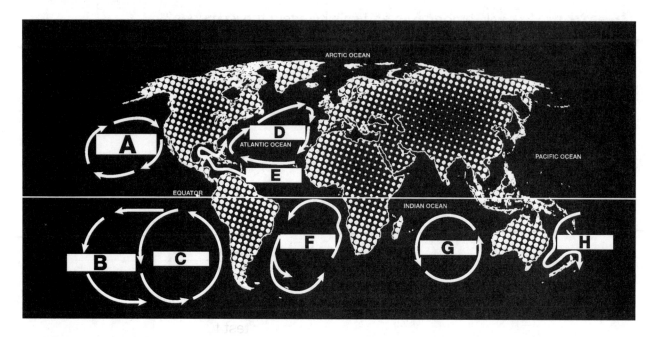

Word Bank	Gulf Stream _____	East Australian _____	Peru _____	North Equatorial _____
	North Atlantic _____	West Australian _____	Brazil _____	South Equatorial _____

2. What are many currents named after? _____

3. What is noticeable about how the currents rotate in the Northern Hemisphere versus the Southern Hemisphere?

_____

_____

4. Why do most currents travel in these circular patterns?

_____

_____

Name _____

Density Lab

Experiment with layering solutions of different densities. Put them in order from the most dense to the least dense.

Question: How can I determine the correct order, from most dense to least dense, of these solutions?

Hypothesize: _____

_____

Test It:

1. Examine the solutions your teacher has distributed. Can you identify any of the

   liquids simply by smelling them? _____ If so, which color? _____

   What do you think it is? _____

2. Layer different colored liquids in the test tube. Hold the test tube at an angle so that you do not disturb the surface of the liquid in the tube. Write down the first letter of each color in the space provided, with the first color on the bottom, the second color next, and so on.

3. As soon as the colors mix, pour the liquid from your test tube into the waste beaker or disposable cup and start another trial. For the next trial, be sure to put the most dense liquid from your previous trial in first.

4. Continue until you can determine the proper order, from most dense to least dense.

5. Record the correct order in one of the trial diagrams below.

   Data: (Y = YELLOW, G = GREEN, B = BLUE, R = RED)

Trial 1	Trial 2	Trial 3	Trial 4	Trial 5	Trial 6	Trial 7	Trial 8	Trial 9	Trial 10

Analyze and Conclude:

6. What was your final order of colors, from bottom to top?

   _____

7. Which of these colors indicated the most dense solution? _____

   the least dense? _____

8. Was your prediction correct? _____

Name _____

Salinity Lab

The density of water is directly related to the salinity of that water. Keep this fact in mind as you perform the following investigation. Experiment with layering solutions of different salinities.

Question: Will solutions with varying salinities layer according to density like the solutions with different densities?

Hypothesize: Will the solution with the highest salinity have the greatest or

lowest density? _____

Test It:

1. Examine the solutions your teacher has distributed. Can you identify any or all of

   them? _____ If so, list them here. _____

2. Repeat the procedure from the density lab on the previous page by layering different colors of liquids. Write down the first letter of each color in the spaces below. As soon as the colors mix, dump out your test tube in a waste beaker or disposable cup and start over. For the next trial, put the liquid with the highest density in first.

3. Determine the correct order of the liquids from saltiest (most dense) to least salty (least dense). Record it in the trial diagrams below.

   Data: (Y = YELLOW, G = GREEN, B = BLUE, R = RED)

Trial 1	Trial 2	Trial 3	Trial 4	Trial 5	Trial 6	Trial 7	Trial 8	Trial 9	Trial 10

Analyze and Conclude:

4. What was the final order of the colors that you determined, from bottom to top?

   _____

5. Why do you think this order occurred? _____

6. Which percent solution was the most dense? _____

7. Which percent solution was the least dense? _____

8. Where in the ocean would the saltiest water be found? _____

9. Compare your hypothesis to the results. _____

9.6C
NOTEBOOK

Name _____

Directions: Cupcake Core Samples

Ships like the *JOIDES Resolution* have faced tremendous obstacles as they try to observe below Earth's surface. After all, the only layer of the earth that people have ever been able to actually observe is the crust. However, research geologists try to learn what is under the crust by taking what they call *core samples*. Using specially designed tube-shaped tools, a geologist takes a small sample of the earth in order to find the composition of the rocks, samples of fossils, and any other useful information that might apply to the job that the geologist is working on.

Use basic core sampling techniques to learn what kinds of layers are in an unknown sample—a cupcake—by following the directions below.

1. Organize the materials from your teacher. Set the waxed paper or foil down first and then arrange the other items on top of that surface.

2. Fold your piece of drawing paper into four sections. Label one section *Hypothesis*. Then label the other sections *Sample 1*, *Sample 2*, and *Sample 3*.

3. In the Hypothesis section, draw what you think a cross section of your cupcake will look like. How many layers do you think it will have? How thick will they be? What colors?

4. To take your first core sample of the cupcake, slowly push a straw down through the layers of the cupcake. Then hold your finger over the top of the straw and pull it out very carefully. What you should have inside the straw is your core Sample 1 (S1 in the diagram).

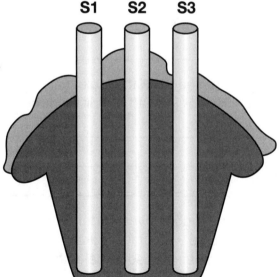

5. Remove your finger from the end of the straw. Point the straw toward your piece of construction or drawing paper and gently blow into the straw. Set your core sample on the appropriately labeled section of paper and make a sketch of it.

6. Repeat the core sample procedure two more times, drawing your observations in the sections labeled Sample 2 and Sample 3 (S2 and S3 in the diagram to the right).

7. Once you complete the drawings, use the piece of dental floss to slowly and carefully slice your cupcake in half from the top to the bottom.

© Science Level 5 • Earth's Processes

Name _____

Analyzing Cupcake Core Samples

Complete the exercises below.

1. Compare your core samples to the cross section of the cupcake. How accurate were your drawings?

   _____

   _____

2. How many layers did you count in the drawings of your cupcake core samples?

   _____

3. How many layers did you count when you sliced your cupcake in half?

   _____

4. According to your teacher, how many layers were actually in your cupcake?

   _____

5. In geological terms what could you compare the straws to?

   _____

6. In geological terms what could you compare the cupcake to?

   _____

7. Why do you think that scientists have tried to get to the mantle by drilling through the ocean floor instead of drilling through the earth's crust on dry land?

   _____

   _____

   _____

8. If your teacher gives permission and if you have no food allergies, taste your cupcake and guess what flavors are in it. Write them here and then ask your teacher what types of batter were used to bake the cupcakes.

   _____

   _____

   _____

Name _____

Magnetic Reversals

After you have obtained the necessary materials from your teacher, follow the directions below to model the magnetic reversals on the ocean floor.

1. Divide one color of play dough into four sections. Call this *Color A*.

   Record the color here: _____

2. Divide the other color of play dough into five sections. Call this *Color B*.

   Record the color here: _____

3. Using the waxed paper or foil square as a working surface, roll each section of play dough into a long, thin section about 15 cm (6 in.) long.

4. Start by placing one roll of Color B in the center of the waxed paper or foil. Flatten it slightly.

5. Next, take two rolls of Color A. Place one on each side of the flattened roll from Step 4. Flatten them slightly and be sure that they touch the first section but do not overlap too much.

6. Repeat, but with two rolls of Color B on the outside.

7. Repeat this procedure with two rolls of Color A and then two more rolls of Color B.

8. Using the plastic knife, carefully cut the center roll (Color B) lengthwise and slightly spread the two sections of play dough apart.

9. When you are finished, ask your teacher to check your work.

10. What do the colored sections of play dough represent?

   _____

11. To what scientific theory does this exercise relate?

   _____

12. Write the definition of *polarity* here.

   _____

13. Describe what geologists have discovered about magnetic polarity on the ocean floor.

   _____

   _____

   _____

Name _____

Making a Compass

Use the materials from your teacher to follow the directions below.

1. Place the piece of cork on top of the water in the pie pan.

2. Rub the needle on the magnet in the same direction approximately 50 times.

3. Lay the needle on the center of the cork piece.

4. Watch what happens to the needle.

5. Pick up the needle. Rub it 50 times on the magnet in the same direction.

6. Place it on the center of the cork piece again.

7. Observe what happens to the needle.

8. What happened to the needle when you placed it on the cork each time?

_____

_____

9. Why did this happen?

_____

_____

10. Write a hypothesis about what might happen if the needle were not made magnetic.

_____

_____

11. Place the needle on the cork piece again, but do not rub it on the bar magnet first.

12. Was your hypothesis from Exercise 10 correct? Explain why.

_____

_____

Name _____

Vocabulary Review

For each of the definitions listed below, choose the correct vocabulary word by filling in the circle beside that term.

1. the process by which one lithospheric plate is forced under another
○ deep ocean current   ○ subduction   ○ polarity

2. a type of igneous rock that cools quickly and has small crystals
○ intrusive   ○ extrusive   ○ rock cycle

3. a climate event in the Pacific Ocean caused by wind shifts, resulting in unusually warm water temperatures
○ El Niño   ○ fossils   ○ salinity

4. a large, nearly flat region of a deep ocean basin
○ abyssal plain   ○ seamount   ○ El Niño

5. the crust and solid, upper portion of the mantle
○ Coriolis effect   ○ seamount   ○ lithosphere

6. the presence of two opposing poles or ends, especially when related to magnets and batteries
○ polarity   ○ subduction   ○ upwelling

Complete the exercise below on a separate sheet of paper.

7. Create your own review sheet using the words *Coriolis effect*, *deep ocean current*, *intrusive*, *lava*, *seamount*, and *upwelling*. Write a multiple choice, matching, or fill-in-the-blank activity, or devise a totally unique worksheet for reviewing these six vocabulary terms. Write your answers on a separate piece of paper. Tell your teacher when you are finished. (Use this space below to brainstorm some ideas.)

Name _____

Chapter 9 Review

Follow the directions and complete the exercises below.

1. Draw a basic diagram of the rock cycle. Include the following terms. Some will be used more than once:
   a. *Igneous*
   b. *Sedimentary*
   c. *Metamorphic*
   d. *eroding, layering, compacting, and cementing*
   e. *melting, cooling, and hardening*
   f. *heat and pressure*

2. Add arrows to these boxes to illustrate each boundary type. Under each diagram write one continental or oceanic feature that might form near that type of boundary.

   Convergent   **Divergent**   **Transform**

   | | | | | | | | |

   _____   _____   _____

3. Turn to *The Rock Cycle* lesson in Chapter 9 and list all examples of specific rocks. Tell which of the three rock types each is. (example: obsidian–igneous)

   _____

   _____

   _____

   _____

   _____

Name _____

Chapter 9 Review, continued

Complete the exercises below.

4. What kinds of natural disasters can be described by the plate tectonics theory?

_____

5. What kinds of weather conditions can be linked to El Niño events?

_____

_____

6. What important characteristics of water allow ocean currents to flow normally?

_____

7. What mineral is known to orient itself toward magnetic north? _____

Why is this mineral so important to geologists?

_____

_____

8. What situation causes an upwelling to occur?

_____

9. Why are fossils only found in sedimentary rocks?

_____

_____

10. What instrument is used to measure liquid density? _____

11. Describe what happens when a plate is subducted.

_____

_____

_____

_____

Name _____

Chapter 9 Review, continued

12. Sketch three ocean features in the spaces below and label each drawing.

_____

_____

_____

Name _____

Survivor Game

You are going to participate in a deserted island survival game. Read and follow each step. Complete the exercises.

1. List as many things as you can think of that you use on a regular basis and believe you need in order to survive. Include items that you think you just cannot live without.

_____

_____

2. List at least five basic needs that all humans have.

_____

_____

3. Which of the items that you listed in Exercise 1 fit into the basic needs that you listed in Exercise 2?

_____

_____

4. Make a list of all the resources you think you will need to survive on a deserted island.

_____

_____

_____

Imagine that your classroom is a deserted island and you are now stranded on it. The next ship will not pass by for a whole week. You are hungry and you know it will be getting dark and cold soon. You must quickly go search for some resources. You will need food, shelter, water, and a way to keep warm and cook food.

5. Look over your list in Exercise 4. Consider your needs of food, water, shelter, keeping warm, and cooking food. Make yourself a new list of the resources you hope to find in your search. Remember, you will need enough supplies for one week. Be as specific as you can.

_____

_____

_____

_____

Name _____

Survivor Game, continued

You are now going on a resources treasure hunt. Listen for directions from your teacher. You will need to find the following supplies in order for you to survive for one week:

14,000 calories of food	10 kg (22 lb) of firewood	50 tree branches
26 L (7 gal) of water	1 pack of matches	100 banana leaves
20 logs		

6. Compare what you found in the resources treasure hunt to what you need to survive.

FOUND	STILL NEED
_____	_____
_____	_____
_____	_____
_____	_____
_____	_____

7. Your class has now been divided into four groups. Each group has been given a designated area on the island in which to build a shelter and live. Why do you think you were put into groups and told where to live? Why could the whole class not stay together? Think of your basic needs.

_____

_____

8. There are no more resources left on the island. You must figure out a way to solve the dilemma of not having enough supplies. Work cooperatively with the other students in your group to solve this problem. If you need to, you may go visit other groups. How are you going to make sure you have enough food, firewood, water, and items to build shelter? Write down your plan. Be specific.

_____

_____

_____

_____

_____

Name _____

Fueling Up

1. Fill in the boxes to construct a concept map that compares the different fossil fuels.

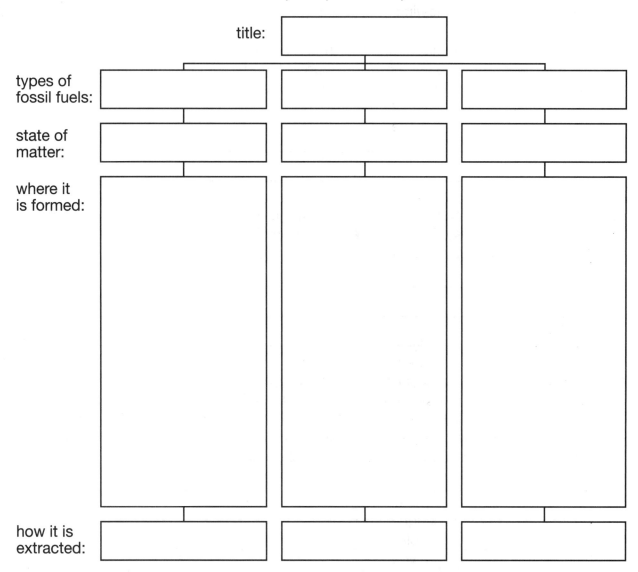

title:

types of
fossil fuels:

state of
matter:

where it
is formed:

how it is
extracted:

2. Consider the states of matter and densities of the three different fossil fuels. If they were to be found all in the same area, how would they settle in layers inside the earth? Label each fossil fuel on the line that represents how deep in the earth it settled.

_____

_____

_____

Name _____

Making a Difference

Read each scenario about how Americans use energy created by fossil fuels. Then on the lines provided, write ideas about how to save energy.

1. The average home uses about one-fourth of a month's electricity to power the clothes washer and dryer. For every load of laundry done in cold instead of hot water, enough energy is saved to power your television for 34 hours!

_____

_____

_____

2. There are over 200 million motor vehicles in the United States alone. Motor vehicles burn fuels such as gasoline and diesel for energy. Burning fossil fuels causes pollution and the excess production of carbon dioxide, a greenhouse gas.

_____

_____

_____

3. On average an American family opens their refrigerator 22 times a day. This means that their refrigerator is opened over 8,000 times a year. When the door is open, the cold air escapes and is replaced by the warm air in your house. More electrical energy is needed to cool it down again. The temperature in refrigerators is often set too cold. The temperature should be set between 3°C and 4.5°C (38°F and 40°F).

_____

_____

_____

4. When cooking with an oven, 25°—50° of temperature is lost every time the door is opened. It takes more energy to heat the oven back up. Microwaves and toaster ovens use less energy than regular ovens. Since it takes longer for an uncovered pot of water to boil than a covered pot of water, more energy is used.

_____

_____

_____

Name _____

Cookie Mining

Read the list of rules below before getting started. The object of the activity is to mine as many chocolate chips as possible to end up with the most profit. Obtain money and materials from your teacher to use in the extraction of ores simulation. Fill in the blanks with your mining data.

Cookie Mining Rules:
1. You will receive $19 to purchase mining equipment and one cookie for your mine, and to pay other mining fees.
2. You cannot use your fingers to hold the cookie when mining for chips. The mining equipment and the paper towel are the only things that are allowed to touch the cookie.
3. You will have a maximum of 5 min to mine the chocolate chips. Keep track of how many minutes you use to mine the cookie.
4. You may purchase as many mining tools as you desire. If a tool breaks, it must be discarded and a new one purchased.
5. The player with the most money at the end of the activity wins. Once you have completed the exercises, you may eat your cookie!

Costs			
Generic cookie	$3	Flat toothpick	$2
Premium cookie	$5	Round toothpick	$4
Cost of mining per minute	$1	Paper clip	$6
Cost of reclamation per square	$1		

1. Observe and select one of the two cookie mines available. The generic cookie usually has fewer chocolate chips than the premium cookie, but the premium cookie costs more. ***Cookie type*** _____ ***Price of cookie mine*** _____

2. Select and purchase the tool(s) you want to use. Record the costs of the equipment.

Flat toothpick _____ × $2 = _____

Round toothpick _____ × $4 = _____

Paper clip _____ × $6 = _____

Total equipment costs _____

3. Place the cookie on graph paper. Outline your cookie with a pencil. Count the number of squares, including the partial squares that fall inside the circle. Record the number. _____

Name _____

Cookie Mining, continued

4. Put the cookie on the paper towel. This is the last time you can touch the cookie with your fingers. Use your tools to mine the chips. You have 5 min. You will receive $2 for each chip mined. All broken chips can be combined to make only one chip.

Mining costs _____ minutes × $1 = _____

Number of chips _____ × $2 = _____ (value of chips)

5. Find a way to put the pieces of cookie that are left back into the circled area on the graph paper without touching them with your hands. Outline the mined cookie remains. Each square over the original number of squares in Exercise 3 will cost $1.00 in reclamation fees.

Number of squares _____ × $1 = _____ (reclamation fees)

6. Find the total cost of mining.

Cost of mine _____ + Cost of equipment _____ +

Mining costs _____ + Reclamation fees _____ =

_____ Total cost of mining

7. Calculate your profit or loss.
Original cash of $19 + Value of chips _____ = _____ (cash and income)

Cash and income _____

Total cost of mining – _____

Profit or loss = _____

8. What did the cookie represent? _____ What did the

chocolate chips represent? _____

9. What did the cookie look like after it was mined? _____

_____

10. How does this relate to actual mining for nonrenewable resources?

_____

11. With your answer to Exercise 10 in mind, give one reason why people should conserve and protect natural resources.

_____

_____

_____

Name _____

Reduce, Reuse, Recycle

Read each description and identify which of the three Rs are taking place.

1. Double bag your groceries only when it is absolutely necessary. _____

2. Write on both sides of your paper. _____

3. Place your food scraps into a compost pile. _____

4. Take your cans to an aluminum recycling center. _____

5. Donate your old games, books, and toys. _____

6. Walk or ride your bike instead of having someone drive you. _____

7. Buy bulk food items. _____

8. Donate or give away outgrown clothing to someone else. _____

9. Return used computer printer cartridges to the company for refilling.

_____

10. Turn off lights when you are not in the room. _____

Think of other ways you can reduce, reuse, and recycle. Write them below.

11. Reduce

_____

_____

_____

12. Reuse

_____

_____

_____

13. Recycle

_____

_____

_____

10.5B
NOTEBOOK

Name _____

Promoting the Three Rs

You have just been elected as the chairperson of a city-wide committee whose purpose is to reduce, reuse, and recycle. Decide what your goals are and how the committee could promote the goals so that others in the community would join in the efforts. Write a proposal. Use both vocabulary words from this lesson and at least two other vocabulary words from this chapter.

_____

_____

_____

_____

_____

_____

_____

_____

_____

_____

_____

_____

_____

_____

_____

_____

_____

_____

_____

_____

_____

_____

_____

_____

Name _____

Mineral Properties

Minerals are natural resources that are determined by their properties. By performing several tests, mineralogists can identify specific types of minerals. In this activity you will be investigating the properties of color, streak, and hardness. You will visit seven different stations, each with a different mineral. First, examine the mineral located at the station and record its color. Then follow the directions on the following Science Notebook page to perform the streak and hardness tests. Use the information found on the Hardness Scale to determine the hardness of the mineral specimens. Record your findings in the Data Chart below. Remember to handle all sharp objects very carefully.

Data Chart

mineral	color	streak	hardness
iron pyrite			
quartz			
sphalerite (zincblende)			
gypsum			
feldspar			
talc			
crocoite			

Name _____

Testing Minerals

Read the information carefully to perform each test. Record your data on **Science Notebook 10.6A Mineral Properties**.

Streak Test

A streak is the color of a mineral in its powdered form. It is usually obtained by scraping the mineral against a streak plate or an unglazed porcelain tile to see the mark it leaves behind. A mineral's streak color can often be different than its natural color.

1. Make sure the unglazed side of the streak plate or porcelain tile is facing up.

2. Pick up the mineral and hold it tightly in your hand. Place the streak plate on the table or desk and hold the streak plate with your other hand.

3. Scrape the mineral across the streak plate. You may need to do this a few times. Look for the color of the streak. If you cannot see anything, it is probably because the tile is white and the streak color is white. If so, identify the mineral's streak color as white.

4. Record the streak color in the Data Chart.

Hardness Test

A mineral's hardness is its resistance to scratching or being scratched. The Mohs Hardness Scale is used to determine the hardness of a mineral. The scale ranges from 1–10, or softest to hardest. You will be using a version of the Mohs Hardness Scale to identify each mineral's hardness. Follow each step on the next page very carefully. Remember to use your tools responsibly. Once you have determined the mineral's hardness, record the number in the Data Chart.

Hardness Scale

characteristic of mineral	hardness number
can be scratched with a fingernail and rubs off on fingers	1
can be scratched with a fingernail	2
can be scratched with a copper coin	3
can be scratched with a knife blade or sharp nail	4, 5
can be scratched with a steel file	6
can scratch glass	7, 8
scratches most or all other materials	9, 10

Name _____

Testing Minerals, continued

Step 1. Firmly wipe your fingers back and forth across the smoothest section of the specimen. If it leaves a residue on your fingers, the hardness is a 1. If it does not leave a residue, go to Step 2.

Step 2. Try to scratch the specimen with your fingernail. If it leaves a scratch, the hardness is 2. If it does not, go to Step 3.

Step 3. Use the copper coin to try to scratch the mineral. If it leaves a scratch, it has a hardness of 3. If it does not, go to Step 4.

Step 4. Carefully pick up the nail. Hold it in one hand, while holding the specimen in the other hand. Place the tip of the nail on the rock. Try to scratch it. If it leaves a scratch, the hardness is 4–5. If it does not, go to Step 5.

Step 5. Try to scratch the specimen with the steel file. If it leaves a scratch, the hardness is 6. If it does not, go to Step 6.

Step 6. Hold the rock in your hand and try to scratch the piece of glass. If it scratches the glass, it has a hardness of 7 or above. If it does not scratch the glass, the hardness is 6 or below.

Analyze the data in your chart and complete the following exercises.

1. Which mineral was the softest? _____

2. Which mineral was the hardest? _____

3. How many minerals tested could be scratched with the copper coin? _____

4. How many minerals had a streak color that was white? _____

5. Why do you think it is important to do more than one test before determining what kind of mineral it is?

_____

6. Do you think that a mineral that has a hardness between 1–3 can be used to cut objects? Why or why not?

_____

7. Which mineral did you find most interesting? Why?

_____

_____

Name _____

Oily Oil

Petroleum is a natural resource more commonly known as *crude oil*. It is a fossil fuel with unique properties. Another kind of oil comes from vegetables. After receiving materials from your teacher, follow the directions below to investigate some properties of oil. Complete the exercises.

1. Write the word *oil* on a piece of paper towel. Use the eyedropper and squeeze one drop of motor oil onto the paper. Describe the motor oil.

   _____

2. Write the word *water* on another piece of paper towel. Use a different eyedropper and squeeze one drop of water onto the paper. Describe the water.

   _____

3. Put both paper towels under a light or near a sunny window. Allow them to dry.

4. While you are waiting, squeeze a drop of motor oil onto your finger. Rub your thumb and finger together. How does the motor oil feel?

   _____

5. Rinse your fingers in a glass of water. Does the motor oil come off? _____

6. How do your fingers feel now? _____

7. Squeeze a drop of vegetable oil on your finger. Rub your thumb and finger together. How does it feel?

   _____

8. Use a paper towel to wipe off any oil that may still be on your hands. Throw it away.

9. How is the vegetable oil different from the motor oil? How is it the same?

   _____

   _____

10. Get the pieces of paper from under the light or near the window. Observe them. Which one evaporated—the oil or the water? Which one stayed on the paper?

    _____

11. Based on your observations of the properties of oil, what do you think oil can be used for? Why?

    _____

    _____

Name _____

Solar Cooking

The sun is hot and it has a great deal of energy. Can it produce enough energy to cook food? Read the question below and write your prediction. Obtain materials from your teacher and follow the directions carefully.

Question: Can I use solar energy to cook food in a pizza box?

Hypothesize: Record your hypothesis and explain why. _____

_____

Test It:

1. Make sure the pizza box is folded into its designed shape. Place a sheet of notebook paper in the center of the lid and trace around it, creating a rectangle.

2. Use scissors to cut the lid along three sides of the rectangle. Gently fold the flap back along the uncut edge. Cover the underside of the flap with a piece of aluminum foil. Tape the foil to the lid but allow only a very small amount of tape to show on the foil side of the flap.

3. Line the bottom of the box with aluminum foil. Cover the foil with black construction paper and tape into place. Roll up some newspapers and fit them around the inside edges of the box. Tape the newspapers into place.

4. Cut two pieces of plastic wrap 3 cm (1 in.) larger than the flap opening on the lid. Tape one piece of plastic wrap to the underside of the lid, covering the opening. Make sure the plastic is stretched tightly. Close the lid. Tape the other piece of plastic wrap on the top of the lid opening. Make sure the plastic wrap is tight and the edges are completely sealed by the tape.

5. You have now made a solar oven! Take the oven, an aluminum pie plate, and a ruler outside. Place the solar oven at an angle facing the sun.

6. Open the box and place the pie plate in the oven. Pour 150 mL (5 oz) of water into the pie plate. Use a thermometer to take the temperature of the water. Record the temperature.

_____

7. Close the box. Use a ruler to prop the flap open. Make sure the oven is facing the sun and the sun's rays are hitting the oven. Wait 30 to 45 min. Answer Exercises 1–4 in the *Analyze and Conclude* section while you are waiting.

8. Take the water's temperature again and record it.

_____

Name _____

Solar Cooking, *continued*

9. Use pot holders to remove the pie plate with water and set aside. Place two graham crackers side by side in the solar oven. Put one marshmallow on top of one graham cracker and arrange six chocolate chips on top of the other graham cracker. Face the oven toward the sun.

10. Close the lid. Check the food every 10 minutes until the chips have melted and the marshmallow is soft. Put the two graham crackers together and enjoy the treat!

Analyze and Conclude:

1. What is the purpose of lining the underside of the flap with aluminum foil?

_____

2. What purpose do the rolled up newspaper and the plastic wrap serve?

_____

3. What does the black construction paper do?

_____

_____

4. What makes a solar oven work? Refer to Exercises 1–3 in your answer.

_____

_____

_____

_____

5. Did the temperature of the water in the oven increase after 30–45 min? _____

6. What are the benefits of using solar energy as an alternative to fossil fuels?

_____

_____

7. What are the limitations of a solar oven?

_____

_____

Name _____

Vocabulary Review

Unscramble the letters below to identify the vocabulary words. Correctly spell the words in the spaces. Definitions for these words are on the bottom half of the page.

1. NNIAIAOSDELT ___ ___ ___ ___ ___ ___ ___ ___ ___ ___ ___ ___

2. SOPTMOC ___ ___ ___ ___ ___ ___ ___

3. DIALLLNF ___ ___ ___ ___ ___ ___ ___ ___

4. WBNEANERNOLE ___ ___ ___ ___ ___ ___ ___ ___ ___ ___ ___ ___

5. UPMERTLEO ___ ___ ___ ___ ___ ___ ___ ___ ___

6. YNOBCRAHRDO ___ ___ ___ ___ ___ ___ ___ ___ ___ ___ ___

7. SBMOSIA ___ ___ ___ ___ ___ ___ ___

8. BELEWERNA ___ ___ ___ ___ ___ ___ ___ ___ ___

Read the clues below. Write the number of the vocabulary word found above in the space that matches the clue.

9. ___ organic matter that is typically burned as a source of energy

10. ___ substances used by humans, such as fossil fuels, that cannot be renewed

11. ___ an area for depositing garbage that is lined on the bottom and sides

12. ___ a process carried out on ships and land to produce freshwater

13. ___ liquid, usually black, which is a source of fuel

14. ___ organic matter mixed with other substances and used as a fertilizer

15. ___ wood, soil, air, sun, and water

16. ___ a compound consisting of carbon and hydrogen

Name _____

Chapter 10 Review

1. Circle the word for the material below that can conduct heat and electricity.

a. mineral   **b.** gas   **c.** metal

2. List the nonrenewable resources mentioned in this chapter. _____

_____

3. Paper is made from a natural resource. Give one example each of how you can reduce, reuse, and recycle paper.

a. _____

b. _____

c. _____

4. Compare and contrast coal, petroleum, and natural gas since they are all considered

fossil fuels. _____

_____

_____

5. How are each of the three fossil fuels obtained? _____

_____

_____

6. Is it safe to throw everything away in landfills? Why or why not?

_____

_____

7. How is solar energy used as a natural resource? _____

_____

8. What is geothermal energy and what is it used for? _____

_____

_____

9. Why is it important to conserve and protect natural resources?

_____

_____

_____

Name _____

Word Wonders

Look up the words in the dictionary. Write the letter of the matching definition on the blank next to the word.

1. pampero ____

2. contrail ____

3. bora ____

4. simoom ____

5. chinook ____

a. a streak of condensed water vapor by an airplane flying at high altitudes

b. a warm wind occurring along the Pacific coast and the Rocky Mountains, United States

c. a hot, dry, violent, dusty wind from Asian and African deserts

d. a violent, cold northerly wind of the Adriatic (includes Italy and the Balkans)

e. a strong, cold wind that sweeps over the pampas of Argentina

6. What do these words have in common?

_____

Look at the map below. Find the different areas noted in your definitions from above. Mark the map with the defined word in the location that it refers to.

Name _____

Air Dare

Use **BLM 11.1B Directions: Air Dare Experiments** to perform the experiments on this notebook page. Complete the exercises after each experiment.

Experiment 1

Put the empty bottle with the attached funnel on the table. Quickly pour the entire container of water directly into the funnel. Observe what happens.

1. What happened to the water? _____

2. Why do you think that happened? _____

3. Based on this experiment, write a deduction about air. _____

_____

Experiment 2

Hold the string with the meterstick out in front of you. Have another person in your group use a pin to gently and carefully poke a hole through the tape into the balloon. The tape should keep the balloon from popping. Observe the meterstick and the balloons.

4. What happened to the balloon that was punctured? _____

5. What happened to the meterstick? _____

6. Why do you think that happened? _____

7. Based on this experiment, write a deduction about air. _____

_____

Experiment 3

Perform Steps 1–2 on BLM 11.1B again. This time remove your finger but quickly put it back on the straw. Repeat this several more times. Observe what happens.

8. What happened to the water when you took your finger off the straw?

_____

9. What happened when you quickly put your finger on and then took it off the straw?

_____

10. Why do you think that happened? _____

_____

11. Based on this experiment, write a deduction about air. _____

Name _____

Global Winds

Complete the following exercises.

1. Use the terms *unequal heating*, *air pressure*, and *convection currents* to describe how global winds form.

_____

_____

_____

_____

2. Explain what the Coriolis effect is and how it affects global winds.

_____

_____

_____

3. Read the following descriptions. Use the Word Bank to help identify the calm areas and wind belts. Write the correct term in the blank.

Word Bank	doldrums	horse latitudes	trade winds	westerlies	polar easterlies

_____ These winds flow toward the poles and often bring moist air and precipitation.

_____ This is an area of high pressure located at 30°N and 30°S.

_____ These winds are very cold and sink toward the lower latitudes.

_____ This is an area of low pressure located near the equator.

_____ These cool-air winds sink and blow toward the equator.

Earth

4. The circle represents the world. Draw and label the following: *doldrums, horse latitudes, trade winds, westerlies, polar easterlies*.

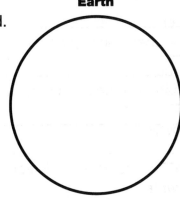

Name _____

Under Pressure

Follow the directions below to complete the activity. Observe the results and answer the questions.

Question: How does a change in air pressure affect a marshmallow?

Hypothesize: What do you think will happen to the marshmallow when the air is sucked out of the bottle?

_____

Test It:

1. Draw a face on both flat ends of a large marshmallow.
2. Drop the marshmallow into the wide-mouthed bottle. You may have to gently squeeze the marshmallow so it goes into the bottle.
3. Approximately 2.5 cm (1 in.) from one end of the straw, wrap the artists' modeling clay to form a ring around the straw. Put that end of the straw into the jar until the clay touches the mouth of the bottle. Mold the clay around the mouth of the bottle to form an airtight seal. It is important that no air is able to get in or out, except through the straw.
4. Suck hard on the straw to remove the air out of the bottle. Have your partner observe what happens.
5. Stop sucking on the straw and observe what happens. Repeat Steps 4–5 several times.
6. Take the straw out of the bottle. Remove the clay from the straw and the bottle. Insert a new straw and have your partner wrap the clay around the straw, as in Step 3. Let your partner perform the activity, following Steps 3–5.

Analyze and Conclude:

1. When you sucked the air out of the bottle, what happened to the air pressure in the bottle?

_____

2. What happened to the marshmallow when you sucked the air out of the bottle?

_____

3. What happened when you stopped sucking on the straw?

_____

4. Explain the reason for the change in the marshmallow.

_____

_____

5. Compare the results of the activity to your prediction.

_____

Name _____

Air Masses

Complete the exercises below.

1. Describe in detail the difference between an air mass and a front. Do they have anything in common?

_____

_____

_____

2. What three uniform characteristics do air masses tend to have?

a. _____ b. _____ c. _____

3. Air masses are identified in part by temperature and humidity. List the two terms used to describe the temperature of an air mass.

a. _____ b. _____

4. List the two terms used to describe the humidity of an air mass.

a. _____ b. _____

Use the world map below to complete the exercise.

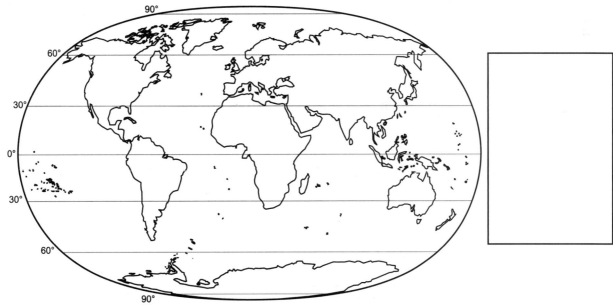

5. Make a legend in the box. Use red for maritime tropical, orange for continental tropical, blue for maritime polar, and green for continental polar. Locate and color at least two areas on the map for each of the four types of air masses. These areas should indicate where each type of air mass might form.

Name _____

Fronts

Answer the exercises.

1. What do air masses tend to do when they meet? Why? _____

_____

_____

2. What forms when two air masses meet? _____

3. Draw a cold front. Explain what happens at a cold front and describe the kind of weather it brings.

_____

_____

_____

_____

_____

_____

_____

_____

_____

_____

4. Draw a warm front. Explain what happens at a warm front and describe the kind of weather it brings.

_____

_____

_____

_____

_____

_____

_____

_____

Name _____

Connecting Isobars

Locate the areas that have the same air pressure. Draw isobars to connect these areas. Illustrate the area of low pressure with an **L**, and the area of high pressure with an **H**.

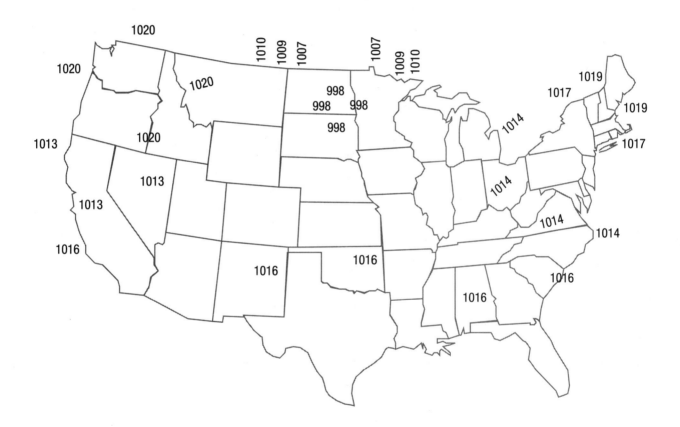

Name _____

Reading Weather Maps

Located on the weather map below are forecasted low and high temperatures in degrees Celsius. Warm and cold fronts are shown too. Analyze the information and complete the exercises.

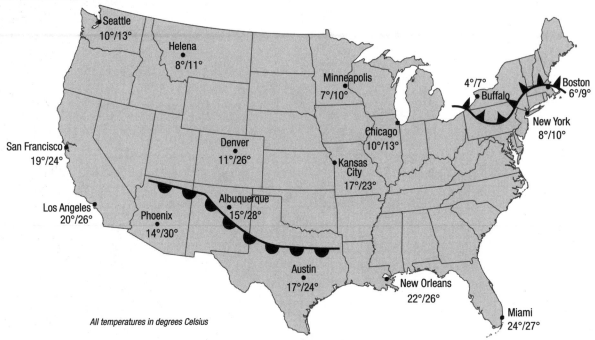

All temperatures in degrees Celsius

1. What city will likely have the highest temperature?

_____

2. What is the forecasted high temperature of that city?

_____

3. What is the forecasted low temperature for Kansas City?

_____

4. Which states have a cold front passing through?

_____

5. What will the weather conditions likely be after the cold front passes?

_____

6. Which states have a warm front passing through?

_____

7. What will the weather conditions likely be while the warm front is passing through?

_____

Name _____

Anemometer

An anemometer is an instrument used to measure wind speed. Wind is the horizontal movement of air. The anemometer acts as an indicator that will spin in the wind and rotate at the same speed as the wind. A real anemometer can give a direct measure of the wind speed. You are going to build a model of an anemometer that will give only an approximate speed of the wind.

Follow the directions below to complete the activity.

1. Use the marker to completely color the outside of one of the cups.

2. Make one hole with the single-hole punch in each of the four cups—about 2 cm ($\frac{3}{4}$ in.) below the rim.

3. Make two holes directly opposite from each other in the fifth cup—about 1.5 cm ($\frac{1}{2}$ in.) below the rim. Punch two more holes in the cup—about 1 cm ($\frac{1}{4}$ in.) below the rim. Make sure the two holes are equally spaced between the first two holes.

4. Insert one of the straws through the hole in one of the first four cups that has only one hole in it. Bend the end of the straw that is inside the cup—about 1.5 cm ($\frac{1}{2}$ in.). Tape it to the inside of the cup.

5. Put the other end of the straw through two opposite holes in the fifth cup. Insert the end of the straw into the hole of a second cup. Tape the end of the straw to the inside of the cup. Make sure that the openings of the two cups face in opposite directions.

6. Repeat Steps 4–5 with the remaining two cups. Slide the straw through the remaining two holes in the fifth cup. Make sure that no two openings on the cups are facing each other. Each of the four cups should be facing sideways.

7. Carefully push the hat pin or T-pin through the two straws.

Name _____

Anemometer, continued

Your model of an anemometer is now ready to use! Follow the directions and complete the exercises.

1. Take the anemometer outside and hold it in front of you in an open area. The center cup should face downward. Keep your eyes focused on the colored cup as it spins around. Have your partner use a stopwatch to time 10-second intervals.

2. Count the number of times the colored cup rotates in 10 sec. Record the number of rotations. _____

3. Repeat Steps 1–2 two more times. Record the number of rotations. _____ _____

4. Average the three rotations and record the number. _____

5. Use the table below to estimate the wind speed. Record the wind speed. _____

6. Use **BLM 11.6A Beaufort Wind Scale** to estimate the Beaufort Force. Record the number. _____

7. Use the Beaufort Wind Scale to find the term and the indicator associated with the wind speed. Record them. _____

rotations in 10 seconds	wind speed (kph)	wind speed (mph)
2–4	2	1
5–7	3	2
8–9	5	3
10–12	6	4
13–15	8	5
16–18	10	6
19–21	11	7
22–23	13	8
24–26	14	9
27–29	16	10
30–32	18	11
33–35	19	12
36–37	21	13
38–40	23	14
41–43	24	15
44–46	26	16

Name _____

Weather Forecasting

Prepare a group weather report to present to the class. Use the map on **Science Notebook 11.6D Group Weather Map** or choose another country to make a weather map for. Follow the guidelines listed below to assist you in preparing the report.

1. Design a weather map for a one-day forecast.
2. Include and label at least 10 cities throughout the country you have chosen.
3. Include the expected high and low temperatures for each of the 10 cities.
4. Use all of the eight precipitation symbols from the *Weather Maps* lesson.
5. Include at least two cold fronts and two warm fronts. Make sure these coincide with the high and low temperatures and precipitation symbols.
6. Draw at least nine isobars to connect areas of the same air pressure. Include the pressure readings. Remember that pressure readings in the 990s to 1000s reflect low pressure. Pressure readings above 1017 indicate areas of high pressure.
7. Identify one high pressure area and one low pressure area. Make sure these areas coincide with the isobars and pressure readings.
8. Present your weather map and forecast to the class. Each member on your team should give a part of the report.
9. Make sure that your oral report fully explains all of the above information. Also include what kind of weather each of the fronts will bring to the areas in which they are located.
10. Decide as a group which of your teammates will complete each of the following jobs and write his or her name down next to the job description.

   • Label the 10 cities. Include the high and low temperatures for each city.
   Student Name: _____

   • Draw the nine isobars with correct pressure readings.
   Student Name: _____

   • Use all eight of the precipitation symbols on the map.
   Student Name: _____

   • Identify two cold fronts and two warm fronts with the correct symbols. Label one high pressure area and one low pressure area after the isobars have been completed. Use the correct symbols for each area. Color the cold front symbol blue and the warm front symbol red. Use blue for the high pressure symbol and red for the low pressure symbol.
   Student Name: _____

11. Each group member should give an oral presentation for the portion of the weather report that he or she designed on the weather map.

Name _____

Group Weather Map

Name _____

Windy Winds

Complete the following exercises.

1. What are three factors that can influence local winds?

a. _____ b. _____ c. _____

2. Why does a valley breeze develop? _____

_____

_____

3. What causes a mountain breeze to occur?

_____

_____

4. Where are the jet streams located?

_____

5. How do the jet streams form? _____

_____

6. Why do airline pilots like to take advantage of the jet streams?

_____

_____

7. Describe the cause of seasonal winds.

_____

_____

8. What is the name given to a common seasonal wind that changes direction with the change of seasons and that usually brings heavy rainfall?

_____

9. If cooler, humid air from over an ocean blows toward dry, warmer air over a continent, what kind of weather will likely occur?

_____

_____

Name _____

Weather Proverbs

Before technology became sophisticated enough to forecast the weather, people would make predictions based on careful observations. Many of these observations were put into rhymes and verbally passed down from generation to generation. Some of these weather proverbs have no scientific basis and are not true. However, some are based on scientific facts and can be used to help predict the weather. Read each weather proverb carefully. Use what you have learned about the atmosphere and the causes and effects of weather to decide if each proverb is true or false. Circle *T* for true and *F* for false. Do your best to explain the reason for your decision.

1. Red sky at night, sailor's delight. Red sky in morning, sailors take warning.   **T**   or   **F**

_____

_____

2. Halo around the sun or moon, rain or snow soon.   **T**   or   **F**

_____

_____

3. When squirrels bring in a big store of nuts, look for a hard winter.   **T**   or   **F**

_____

_____

4. When smoke descends, good weather ends.   **T**   or   **F**

_____

_____

5. When ants travel in a straight line, expect rain; when they scatter, expect fair weather.
   T   or   **F**

_____

_____

6. Clear moon, frost soon.   **T**   or   **F**

_____

_____

Name _____

Vocabulary Review

Write the number of the clue that fits the term on the line in the correct box. If you have correctly matched them all, the sums of the squares in each row, column, and diagonal will be the same.

				Sum
				_____
jet streams _____	sea breeze _____	warm front _____	doldrums _____	**Sum**
mountain breeze _____	westerlies _____	land breeze _____	Coriolis effect _____	**Sum**
horse latitudes _____	wind _____	weather _____	polar easterlies _____	**Sum**
air mass _____	isobar _____	monsoon _____	cold front _____	**Sum**
Sum _____	**Sum** _____	**Sum** _____	**Sum** _____	**Sum** _____

1. strong, high-speed winds in the upper troposphere and lower stratosphere

2. a wind that changes with the seasons

3. used on weather maps to connect areas with the same air pressure

4. not much wind near the equator

5. cold winds blowing from the poles

6. winds between latitudes 30° and 60°

7. a local wind blowing from the land

8. a calm area near 30° latitude

9. causes global winds to curve

10. the movement of air due to differences in air pressure

11. rain, wind, snow, clouds, fair skies

12. afternoon wind blowing toward the valley

13. a large body of air that has similar characteristics

14. the boundary between a fast-moving warm air mass and a slower, cold air mass

15. a local wind blowing toward the land

16. the boundary where a cold air mass sinks under a warm air mass and pushes warm air upward

Name _____

Chapter 11 Review

1. Explain how unequal heating causes local winds and global winds. Be specific.

_____

_____

_____

_____

2. Carefully observe the illustrations below. Use the Word Bank to label each illustration.

| **Word Bank** | sea breeze | land breeze | mountain breeze | valley breeze |

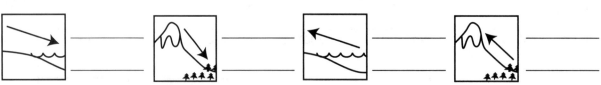

3. Use the Word Bank to label the global winds and calm areas.

| **Word Bank** | trade winds | horse latitudes | doldrums | polar easterlies | westerlies |

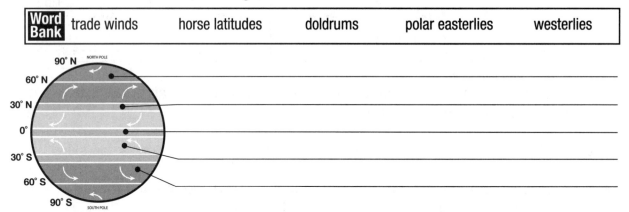

Look at **TM-11.8A Reading Weather Maps** to complete the following exercises.

4. One city's low temperature is the same as another city's high temperature. Which two cities are these?

_____

5. Which city will experience a cold front moving in? _____

6. Which city has the lowest air pressure? _____

7. Which city will probably be experiencing precipitation within the next 24 hours?

_____

8. What is Chicago's forecasted high temperature? _____ Low temperature? _____

Name _____

Moon Words

Listen to your teacher present the following names of the moon and what people believed about it. Write down the information in the space provided.

1. Wolf or Old Moon

_____

2. Snow Moon

_____

3. Worm or Sugaring Moon

_____

4. Pink or Grass Moon

_____

5. Flower or Milk Moon

_____

6. Strawberry or Rose Moon

_____

7. Buck or Thunder Moon

_____

8. Sturgeon or Corn Moon

_____

9. Harvest or Fruit Moon

_____

10. Hunter's or Harvest Moon

_____

11. Beaver or Frost Moon

_____

12. Cold or Long Night Moon

_____

Name _____

Directions: Making and Using an Astrolabe

Making an Astrolabe
Use the materials from your teacher and **BLM 12.1C Reverse Protractor** to construct an astrolabe. Realize that this device is not as accurate as a true astrolabe, but it should estimate the moon's angle from the horizon within 5°–10°.

1. Line up the straight edge of the reverse protractor with one of the longer sides of the cardboard piece and glue the paper protractor to the cardboard.
2. Cut out the cardboard around the protractor. Make sure to cut carefully around the outer black line.
3. Use the paper punch to make a hole in the cardboard at the dark circle, directly below the 0° mark.
4. Tie the washer to one end of the string.
5. Thread the other end of the string through the hole and tie it in place so that the washer extends just beyond the curved edge of the protractor.
6. Tape the straw to the top of the straight edge of the cardboard with two pieces of tape on both ends.
7. The ends of the straw should be even with the edges of the cardboard.

Using an Astrolabe
Now you can use your astrolabe to measure the angle of the moon above the horizon. Follow the directions below as often as possible over the next month, at least once or twice every day.

1. Hold the astrolabe with the straight edge of the cardboard on top, parallel to the ground, with the string hanging down. (If the straight edge is parallel to the ground, then the string should cross the 0° mark on the protractor.)
2. Use one eye to look through the straw at the moon, allowing the string to hang free.
3. With the cardboard astrolabe still in place and the straw pointing toward the moon, wait until the string stops swinging. Then use your index finger and thumb to pinch the string against the cardboard.
4. Use the lines on the protractor to estimate the angle between the moon and the horizon. (For example, if the string is positioned halfway between the 30° and 40° lines, the moon is about 35° above the horizon.)
5. Use your astrolabe tonight to measure the angle and then record it on the moon observation diagram section your teacher gave you. It is best to observe at the same time every day or evening.
6. In addition to shading in the area of the moon you cannot see, check and record the direction in the sky. If you need help understanding which way is north, ask a parent or guardian for help or use a compass.

Name _____

Seasons, Solstices, and Equinoxes

Complete the statements below by using the correct words from the Word Bank.

Word Bank	summer solstice	axis	revolution	spring equinox
	winter solstice	day	rotations	fall equinox

1. During the Northern Hemisphere's _____ the polar axis is tilted, causing the northern part of Earth to receive the sun's most direct rays.

2. The movement of Earth around the sun once a year is called a _____.

3. Earth experiences seasons because it is tilted on its _____ at a 23.5° angle.

4. Around March 21 neither one of Earth's poles or hemispheres are tilted toward the sun. In the Northern Hemisphere, this event is called the _____.

5. As the earth rotates, it experiences one _____ every 24 hours.

6. Around September 22 the Northern Hemisphere experiences the _____ because neither the northern nor the southern part of the earth is closer to the sun.

7. The earth completes a little more than 365 _____ every year.

8. During the Northern Hemisphere's _____ the polar axis is tilted, causing the southern part of Earth to receive the sun's most direct rays.

Name _____

The Sun's Shadow

At the beginning of a sunny day, work with your group to follow the directions and then answer the questions below.

1. Find north using a compass.

2. Have one person stand in a fixed location. Get another group member to use the meterstick to measure one meter directly north of that person. Place a ruler there.

3. Other group members can do the same thing with the three remaining rulers, placing them east, west, and south of the stationary person.

4. Place the meterstick in the ground at the center where the stationary person has been standing. Make sure the meterstick is pointing straight up.

5. Write your hypothesis about how you think the sun's shadow will move throughout

the day. Use complete sentences. _____

_____

_____

6. Record the sun's direction and length of the shadows during regular intervals throughout the day as your teacher allows.

Observation	First	Second	Third	Fourth
time				
direction				
length				

7. How did the direction and length of the shadows change throughout the day?

_____

_____

_____

8. Why did the direction and shadow's length change? _____

_____

_____

9. How might the direction and shadow's length change over the next few days?

Few weeks? Few months? _____

_____

_____

_____

Name _____

Moon Phases

Complete the following activity and exercises.

1. Place the letter of the image on the line next to the correct moon phase. Assume you are looking at the moon from the earth's Northern Hemisphere.

_____full moon   _____waxing crescent
_____new moon   _____third quarter
_____waxing gibbous   _____waning crescent
_____first quarter   _____waning gibbous

A B C D E F G H

2. Draw and label the sun, the earth, and the moon lining up during a new moon phase.

3. Draw and label the sun, the earth, and the moon lining up during a full moon phase.

4. Give two reasons why the different shapes of the moon are visible from Earth.

a. _____

_____

b. _____

_____

Name _____

Lunar and Solar Eclipses

Use your textbook, if necessary, to answer the exercises below.

1. During what phase of the moon does a lunar eclipse occur?

_____

2. Draw a sketch of a lunar eclipse. Color your drawing to include the areas of the sun and the earth's shadows.

3. Why does the moon have a colored hue during a lunar eclipse?

_____

_____

4. During what phase of the moon does a solar eclipse occur?

_____

5. Draw a sketch of a solar eclipse. Color your drawing to include the areas of the sun and the earth's shadows.

6. What is the main difference between a total and a partial eclipse?

_____

_____

_____

12.5A
NOTEBOOK

Name _____

Ins and Outs of Tides

Fill in the blanks to finish the following sentences. You may use your textbook as a reference. Then unscramble the circled letters to complete the word at the bottom of the page.

1. Water bulges at two points on Earth at a time because of the moon's

___ ___ ___ ___ ___ ___ ___.

2. Even though the sun has a greater ___ ___ ___ ___ than the moon, the moon's

gravitational pull on different parts of Earth is the main cause of the ocean's tides.

3. A ___ ___ ___◯ is the periodic rising and falling of the surface level of ocean water.

4. The moon is ___◯___ ___ ___ ___ to the earth than the sun is.

5. Most places on Earth experience ___ ___ ___ high tides and ___ ___ ___ low tides

each day.

6. A ___ ___◯___ tide occurs at the point on Earth that is closest to the moon, as well

as the location opposite of that point.

7. Suppose you drew a line from one high tide to the other and then drew

another line connecting the two low tide areas on Earth. The lines would be

___ ___ ___ ___ ___ ___ ___ ___◯___ ___ ___ to each other.

8. In about a 12-hour cycle, ocean waters in most locations on Earth rise for ___ ___ ___

hours and fall for ___ ___ ___ hours.

BONUS:
Ocean waters do not b ___ ___ ___ ___ as much in the polar regions as they do at
the equator.

© Science Level 5 • Sun, Earth, and Moon

Name _____

Spring and Neap Tides

You may use your textbook as a reference to complete the diagrams and exercises below.

1. Label each diagram below *spring tide* or *neap tide*.
2. Use a red pen or colored pencil to draw a dotted line on each diagram that shows how the sun, the moon, and the earth line up.
3. Label each moon with the correct phase.

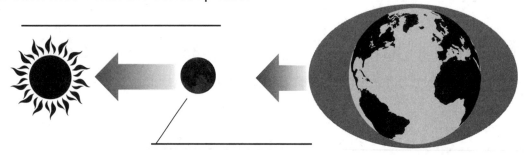

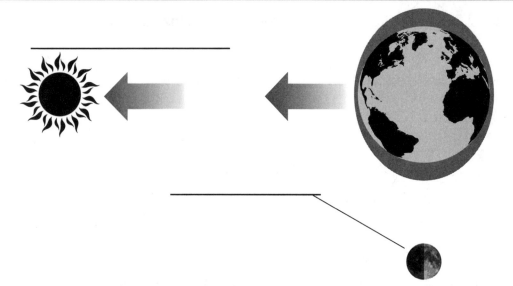

4. Explain the difference between a spring tide and a neap tide.

_____

_____

5. How many times per month do spring and neap tides occur?

_____

6. What location on Earth experiences the largest difference between sea levels of high and low tides?

_____

Name _____

Telescope Basics

Obtain materials from your teacher and listen for directions. Complete the following exercises:

Question: How can I make a telescope using the materials that my teacher has distributed?

Hypothesize: Discuss ideas with your group and record your plan.

_____

_____

Test It:

After you have written down your strategy, try it out by focusing on a well-lit object on the other side of the room or outside your classroom window. Record what you see below.

_____

_____

Analyze and Conclude:

1. What object did you choose to focus on? _____

2. Was the object well-lit? _____

3. Was the object you observed magnified through your lenses? _____

4. Did your strategy work? _____

5. Given the chance to try again, what would you do differently?

_____

_____

6. Try out your revised plan.

7. Record your results.

_____

_____

_____

Name _____

Making a Refracting Telescope

Follow the instructions below to make your own refracting telescope! Be sure that everyone in your group gets a turn to use the materials.

1. Examine the lenses. Find the larger, thinner lens of the two. It must be convex. The larger it is, the more powerful your telescope will be. The thinner it is in the center, the weaker it is. That means that you will be able to see through it more clearly. This is your objective lens.

2. Look at the second lens. It should be smaller and more powerful than your objective lens. It also should be as thick as possible. The thickness gives more power and better vision through the telescope. This is your eyepiece. Name the type of lens it is.

_____

3. Follow your teacher's directions to face a distant, well-lighted object, either inside (like a pencil holder) or outside (like a tree).

4. Hold your eyepiece lens very close to one eye and look through it. Close your other eye if you want to.

5. Hold your objective lens directly in front of the eyepiece lens.

6. Slowly move your objective lens in a straight line away from your eyepiece lens until the object you are viewing comes into view through both lenses. Once you are able to see the object, move the objective lens in and out until you can see your object very clearly. You may need a classmate to move the objective lens out farther than your arms can reach.

7. How did the object appear to change? _____

_____

_____

8. Now repeat this experiment using the foil square with a small pinhole in it as your eyepiece.

9. Compare what you saw using the two different eyepieces, the concave lens, and

the foil. _____

_____

10. Which lens on a telescope is most similar to a lens on eyeglasses? _____

11. What is the other lens similar to? _____

12. In order to make a reflecting telescope, what would you need to do differently?

_____

_____

Name _____

Space Race

Fill in the time line of events, naming the dates, people, or the spacecraft that were part of the Space Race.

date	person	spacecraft
1957	None	
		Explorer 1
	Alan Shepard	
1962		*Friendship 7*
	Neil Armstrong	

1. What does NASA stand for and why was it established?

_____

_____

2. What president challenged the United States to land the first person on the moon?

_____

3. What three astronauts were aboard *Apollo 11*?

  a. _____

  b. _____

  c. _____

4. How many days and kilometers (miles) traveled did it take for these three astronauts to reach the moon?

  _____ days

  _____ kilometers

  _____ miles

5. Who was the first astronaut to walk on the moon? _____

6. Which of *Apollo 11*'s two modules did he step out of? _____

7. What famous words did this astronaut say when he first set foot on the moon?

_____

_____

Name _____

Moon Mapping

Use **TM-12.7B Moon Map** to label the features on the picture below. Then use the Internet, encyclopedias, or other resources to find more places to label. Draw a line out from a certain portion of the moon and then note the name of the feature you found. Be sure you can prove to your teacher that your information is correct! Then complete the exercises below.

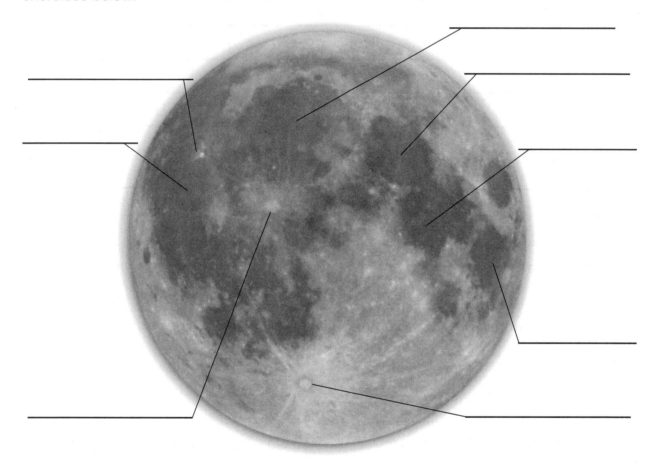

1. What is a dark flat area on the moon's surface called? _____

2. What is it filled with? _____

3. What are the light-colored areas on the moon's surface called? _____

4. Circle a large light-colored area on the image above.

5. What moon feature exists on both the dark and light areas of the moon? _____

6. What is a meteoroid? _____

12.8A
NOTEBOOK

Name _____

Vocabulary Review

Match the following words to the correct descriptions and write them in the blanks below.

Word Bank	law of universal gravitation		spring tide	gibbous	equinox	mare	wane
	tide	solar eclipse	lunar eclipse	crescent	solstice	wax	neap tide

_____ **1.** the periodic rising and falling of the surface of ocean water

_____ **2.** a condition of the greatest difference between low and high tides

_____ **3.** every object in the universe attracts every other object, depending on their masses and distances from one another

_____ **4.** occurs when Earth passes directly between the sun and the moon, causing Earth's shadow to block the sun's light from the moon

_____ **5.** the moon phase in which more than half, but not all, of the moon's sunlit side is visible

_____ **6.** to grow

_____ **7.** the moon phase in which less than half of the moon's sunlit side is visible

_____ **8.** occurs when the moon passes directly between the sun and Earth, causing the moon's shadow to block the sun's light from a portion of Earth

_____ **9.** the two days each year when direct sunlight reaches farthest north or farthest south of Earth's equator

_____ **10.** a dark, flat area on the moon's surface filled with hardened lava

_____ **11.** a condition of the least difference between low and high tides

_____ **12.** the two days each year when day and night are about equal in length

_____ **13.** to shrink

© *Science* Level 5 • Sun, Earth, and Moon

12.8B
NOTEBOOK

Name _____

Chapter 12 Review

Match the correct term with its definition. Write the letter on the blank.

A. Newton's first law of motion

B. orbit

C. mass

D. weight

E. axis

F. meteoroid

G. crater

____ **1.** a measure of how much matter is within an object

____ **2.** an imaginary line that Earth spins on at a 23.5° angle

____ **3.** a measure of the pull of gravity on an object

____ **4.** a rock fragment from an asteroid or comet

____ **5.** the path an object follows as it revolves around another object

____ **6.** a tendency for an object to stay in motion or to stay at rest unless acted upon by an outside force

____ **7.** a large round depression that has been created by the impact of a meteoroid

8. What factor from the list above affects the gravitational pull of an object?

_____

9. Why can humans not live on the moon as they do on Earth?

_____

_____

10. Newton said that two factors combined to affect the moon's orbit around the earth. Name them.

a. _____   **b.** _____

11. The moon makes one rotation in how many days?_____

12. The earth makes one revolution in how many days? _____

13. How long does it take for the earth to rotate one time?_____

14. Write a five-sentence essay that includes at least two facts about the United States' moon mission. Also, make at least one statement about the space race that led to it.

_____

_____

_____

_____

_____

© *Science* Level 5 · Sun, Earth, and Moon

Name _____

Chapter 12 Review, continued

Determine if each statement is true or false. Write *True* or *False* on the line next to the statement. If it is false, write a correct statement underneath.

15. The moon's gravity is about $\frac{1}{6}$ of the earth's gravity. _____

_____

16. The waxing moon phase appears on the right side of the moon from everywhere

on Earth. _____

_____

17. The moon rises and sets at different times every day. _____

_____

18. We can never see a full moon phase from our perspective here on Earth. _____

_____

_____

19. In the Southern Hemisphere many people can enjoy visiting the beach during the

December solstice. _____

_____

20. Equinoxes occur during the months of December and June. _____

_____

21. Highlands on the moon's surface are the lighter parts visible from Earth.

_____

_____

22. Look at the image below and tell what type of eclipse it is and how you know.

_____

_____

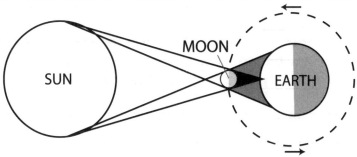

Name _____

Chapter 12 Review, continued

Complete the statements below.

23. Because the moon is _____ to Earth, it has a greater effect on the earth's tides than the sun does, even though the sun has a much greater mass than either the moon or the earth.

24. High tide occurs on _____ sides of the earth at the same time because of the moon's gravitational pull on different parts of the earth.

25. If it were not for _____, the moon could be pulled into the earth because of the earth's gravity. Likewise, the earth might be pulled into the sun and burn up.

Draw diagrams of spring and neap tides in the boxes below. Clearly show the locations of the earth, the sun, and the moon for each sketch by connecting them with dotted lines.

26.

27.

Draw a diagram of the moon phases as seen from the Northern Hemisphere on the left. Be sure that the sun is in the correct location in comparison to Earth during the new and full moon shapes. On the right draw a diagram showing why we experience seasons on Earth. Label two equinoxes, two solstices, and include dates. Create your illustration from a Northern Hemisphere perspective.

28.

29.

30. Since scientists cannot use telescopes to view all of the moon's surface from Earth, what other methods can they use? Name at least two.

_____

_____

Name _____

Metamorphosis

Cut out the pictures and labels from **BLM 13.1A Monarch Butterfly Stages** and glue them onto the appropriate boxes below. Write a one-sentence description of each stage on the lines below each box.

Name _____

Transitions

Fill in the four ovals with the information you have learned regarding adolescence. Add more lines and ovals as needed.

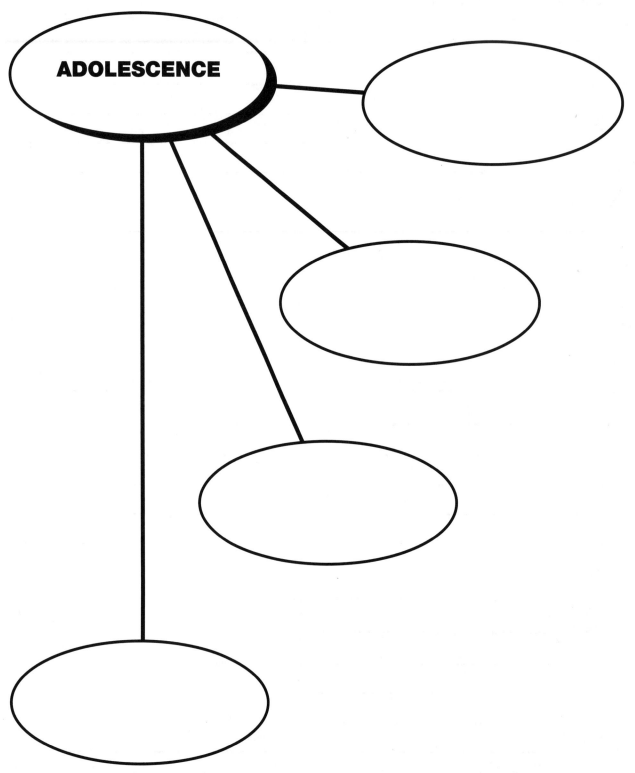

Name _____

Skin Structure and Care

1. Label the illustration below without using your textbook first. Then refer to your textbook, if necessary, to finish labeling and to complete the exercises below.

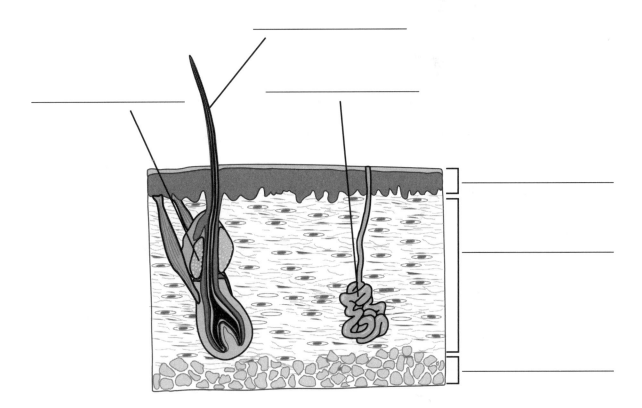

2. List two ways to care for your skin and hair.

a. _____

b. _____

3. Name two things that the sebaceous gland is responsible for.

a. _____   b. _____

Name _____

Skin Function

Answer the following exercises.

1. What is the largest organ in the human body? _____

2. List four functions of the skin.

    a. _____

    b. _____

    c. _____

    d. _____

3. Which layer of skin protects the body from the external environment? _____

4. Which layer contains many nerves, blood vessels, glands, and hairs? _____

5. Which layer contains the pores? _____

6. What lies under the dermis and what does this structure do?

_____

7. Name one positive and one negative thing that sebaceous glands are responsible for.

    a. _____

    b. _____

8. What is one function of the sweat glands? _____

9. How do the sweat glands and sebaceous glands respond during puberty?

_____

_____

10. What causes them to respond in this way?

_____

_____

_____

11. Do the sweat and sebaceous glands release perspiration and sebum into the

bloodstream? _____

Name _____

Growing Your Vocabulary

Place the letter of the correct term from the Word Bank on the line under the description.

Word Bank

a. pituitary gland	**d.** long bone	**g.** fracture
b. growth spurt	**e.** gigantism	**h.** diabetes
c. hypothalamus	**f.** obesity	**i.** genetics

the condition of being more than 20% overweight

1. _____

a gland in the brain that releases growth hormone

4. _____

increase in height and weight during puberty

7. _____

a crack, shattering, or break in a bone

2. _____

overproduction of growth hormone

5. _____

a main factor that determines growth patterns, related to one's parents

8. _____

a disease that involves blood sugar levels and the pancreas

3. _____

a gland in the brain that signals the start of puberty

6. _____

a part of the skeleton found in the arms and legs

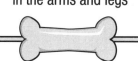

9. _____

Name _____

Broken Bones Survey

As your teacher polls the class, enter tally marks in the chart below.

site of fracture	number of boys	number of girls
arm		
leg		
other		

Brainstorm with your group the best way to illustrate this data with a pictograph. Then draw your pictograph below. Be sure to include a key that defines your symbols.

Hint: You may want to use more than one color for your pictograph symbols.

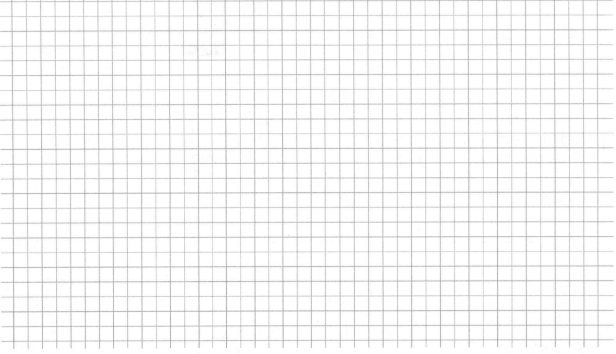

Name _____

Teeth

Use your textbook to complete the exercises below.

1. Label the main parts of the tooth. Use different colored crayons, markers, or pencils to fill in each section of the tooth.

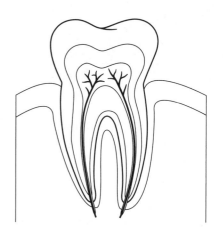

2. Write the different types of teeth on the lines.

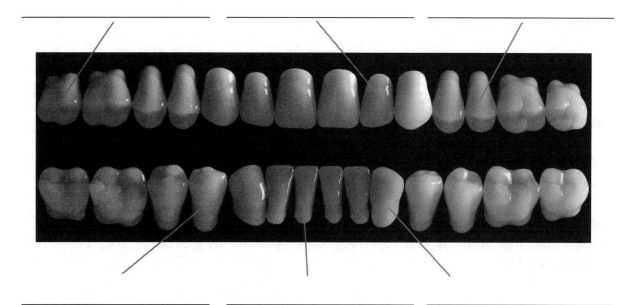

3. Count the teeth above and write which teeth are not shown in the picture.

_____

4. About how old would a person with these teeth be? _____

5. List three main functions of teeth.

    a. _____

    b. _____

    c. _____

Name _____

Oral Care Investigation

 Gooey sweets can stick to the surface of your teeth for long periods of time. This microscopic image is of the sugar molecules that can cause plaque to form and build up. The sugar is digested by bacteria in your mouth and turned into acids that often decay tooth enamel.

Use the plaque disclosing tablets, a toothbrush, floss, and fluoride toothpaste to follow the directions below. The plaque disclosing tablets will show where plaque is present on your teeth.

Question:
How clean are my teeth right now?

Hypothesize:
1. How much plaque is in your mouth at this moment? Describe where you might see the tablets' color after chewing them.

_____

_____

Test It:
• Chew one of the tablets and look in the mirror.
• Brush and floss your teeth.
• Chew another tablet and look in the mirror.

Analyze and Conclude:
2. Describe what you saw when you looked in the mirror the first time. Tell how you felt about what you saw.

_____

_____

3. Explain what you observed after you brushed and flossed your teeth. Is this what you expected?

_____

_____

4. Will you change any daily habits based on what you have just learned? If so, what will you do differently and why?

_____

Name _____

Nutrition Choices

Study the nutrition labels below and use them to complete the exercises.

milk 1%, chocolate

Nutrition Facts
Serving Size 8 fl oz (245g)
Servings Per Container 8

Amount Per Serving

Calories 170   Calories from Fat 20

%Daily Value*

Total Fat 2.5g	4 %
Saturated Fat 1.5g	8 %
Trans Fat 0g	0 %
Cholesterol 5mg	2 %
Sodium 190mg	8 %
Total Carbohydrate 29g	10 %
Dietary Fiber 1g	5 %
Sugars 27g	
Protein 8g	

Vitamin A 10% • Vitamin C 6%

Calcium 30% • Iron 4%

* Percent Daily Values are based on a 2,000 calorie diet.

milk 2%

Nutrition Facts
Serving Size 8 fl oz (245g)
Servings Per Container 8

Amount Per Serving

Calories 130   Calories from Fat 45

%Daily Value*

Total Fat 5g	8 %
Saturated Fat 3g	15 %
Trans Fat 0g	0 %
Cholesterol 20mg	7 %
Sodium 125mg	5 %
Total Carbohydrate 13g	4 %
Dietary Fiber 0g	0 %
Sugars 12g	
Protein 8g	

Vitamin A 10% • Vitamin C 4%

Calcium 30% • Iron 0%

* Percent Daily Values are based on a 2,000 calorie diet.

fruit-flavored yogurt

Nutrition Facts
Serving Size 6 oz (170g)
Servings Per Container 1

Amount Per Serving

Calories 170   Calories from Fat 15

%Daily Value*

Total Fat 1.5g	2 %
Saturated Fat 1g	5 %
Trans Fat 0g	0 %
Cholesterol 10mg	3 %
Sodium 125mg	5 %
Total Carbohydrate 33g	11 %
Dietary Fiber 0g	0 %
Sugars 30g	
Protein 6g	

Vitamin A 0% • Vitamin C 0%

Calcium 20% • Iron 0%

* Percent Daily Values are based on a 2,000 calorie diet.

cottage cheese

Nutrition Facts
Serving Size 4 oz (119g)
Servings Per Container 4

Amount Per Serving

Calories 90   Calories from Fat 20

%Daily Value*

Total Fat 2.5g	4 %
Saturated Fat 1.5g	8 %
Trans Fat 0g	0 %
Cholesterol 15mg	5 %
Sodium 410mg	17 %
Total Carbohydrate 6g	2 %
Dietary Fiber 0g	0 %
Sugars 5g	
Protein 11g	

Vitamin A 4% • Vitamin C 0%

Calcium 8% • Iron 0%

* Percent Daily Values are based on a 2,000 calorie diet.

1. Which kind of milk has the lower number of fat grams? _____

2. Which kind of milk has more calories? _____

3. How much milk do you drink at one time? _____

   Is it more or less than the serving size? _____

4. Compare the calories and sugar grams in fruit-flavored yogurt and cottage cheese.

   Which is lower in sugar? _____

5. Compare the amount of sugar in the yogurt and cottage cheese. Which is the better

   choice? _____

6. What is the serving size for yogurt? _____

   Is that how much you usually eat in one serving? _____

Name _____

Exercise

Healthy lifestyles include a minimum of 30 min of moderate physical activity per day. Review the sample activities listed below. Record all physical activity for one full week. Refer to the list to decide if the activity is moderate or vigorous. Put it in the proper box and record the number of minutes. Complete the exercises at the bottom of the page.

Moderate activity
walking
bicycling/skating
hiking
working in garden or yard

Vigorous activity
jogging/running
swimming laps
playing basketball, football, or soccer

Exercise Log

	Monday	Tuesday	Wednesday	Thursday	Friday	Saturday	Sunday
Moderate List activity and minutes spent.							
Vigorous List activity and minutes spent.							

1. How many days this week were you physically active for at least 30 min? _____

2. Were there any days when you did not make time for moderate exercise? _____

3. What was the total number of minutes you exercised this week? _____

4. How would you rate yourself?

   Circle one: NEEDS IMPROVEMENT   GOOD   EXCELLENT

5. What is your physical activity goal for next week? _____

Name _____

Relaxation

While exercise is important, rest is also part of a balanced life. Read the list below and use the log to record your relaxation time for one full week. Record the number of minutes spent in that activity. Answer the exercises below.

Relaxation Choices

QT: quiet time with God   MT: listening to music

RT: reading   GT: playing sedentary games

Create your own category and assign a two-letter code for it. _____

Personal Relaxation Log

	Monday	Tuesday	Wednesday	Thursday	Friday	Saturday	Sunday
QT minutes spent:							
RT minutes spent:							
MT minutes spent:							
GT minutes spent:							
_____ minutes spent:							

1. How many days this week did you take time to relax? _____

2. How many minutes did you spend relaxing during the week? _____

3. How would you rate yourself? Circle one: NEEDS IMPROVEMENT

                                             GOOD

                                             EXCELLENT

4. Why did you give yourself that rating? _____

5. What is your relaxation goal for next week? _____

Name _____

Weekly Activities

Complete this page and use your results to fill in **BLM 13.6B Pie Chart**.

1. There are 24 hours in a day. How many hours are there in one week?_____
Show your work.

2. Estimate the number of hours per week that you spend in each of the activities listed below. Record the hours on the lines provided below.
Note: Round all times up to the nearest half hour.

3. Follow these steps to calculate the percentage of time per week for each activity.
   a. Divide the number of hours spent on the activity by the total number of hours in a week.
   b. Multiply the decimal number by 100.
   c. Enter your answers on the blank lines next to the percentage sign for each activity.

4. Record the percentages below on the chart at the bottom of BLM 13.6B.

Time spent on activities per week

exercise	_____hr	_____%
relaxation and sleep	_____hr	_____%
school and homework	_____hr	_____%
family time/meals	_____hr	_____%
church/youth group/entertainment	_____hr	_____%
other activities	_____hr	_____%

Name _____

Sleep

Answer each exercise below using complete sentences.

1. Which gland releases a hormone that directly influences the sleep cycle?

_____

2. Summarize how the nervous and endocrine systems work together to affect sleep.

_____

_____

_____

3. How does puberty affect the pineal gland and the hormone that influences sleep?

_____

_____

4. How does this affect adolescents? _____

_____

5. What are some common effects from a lack of proper sleep?

_____

_____

6. Have you ever experienced any of the effects from lack of sleep? Describe what

happened. _____

_____

_____

7. What are the two kinds of sleep?

    a. _____

    b. _____

8. Describe the difference between the two types of sleep.

_____

_____

_____

_____

Name _____

Sleep Log

Proper amounts of sleep are important. Toddlers and preschoolers need about 10–12 hours of sleep per day. Adolescents need about 9–10 hours. Adults need approximately 8 hours each day. Choose one night during the school week and keep a sleep log for each member of your family. Remember to include yourself.

name of family member	time the person went to bed	time the person got out of bed in the morning	number of hours slept	woke up during the night		number of caffeinated beverages consumed during the day
				yes	no	

1. How many family members got the recommended amount of sleep?

_____

2. If any did not, how did it affect their day?

_____

_____

_____

3. If anyone drank caffeinated beverages, did it affect his or her sleep in any way? Explain.

_____

_____

_____

Name _____

Vocabulary Review

ACROSS

2 an area of tooth decay caused by prolonged exposure to bacteria

3 a fluid released by the sweat glands

8 a chemical messenger that creates a response in the body

9 an oil produced by glands located in the skin

10 a specialized tissue that produces and releases chemicals

11 the third molars, usually the last teeth to appear

12 the period of time between childhood and adulthood

DOWN

1 a gland that stimulates growth and development

4 the system made of a network of glands that helps to regulate body functions

5 a skin condition that results when mostly excess sebum clogs skin pores

6 the process of physical changes as a child's body develops into an adult

7 one of several elongated parts of the human skeleton

8 a state of balance within a cell, organ, or system

13.8B
NOTEBOOK

Name _____

Chapter 13 Review

1. Place the letter of the correct gland description on the line.

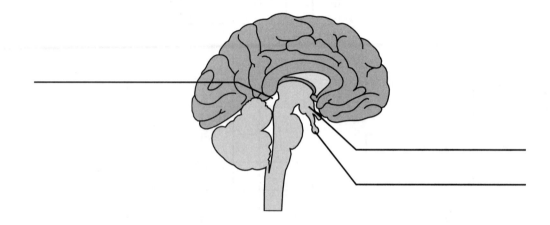

a. This gland gives orders to the pituitary gland.

b. This is called *the master gland* because it controls many other glands.

c. This tiny gland secretes a hormone that affects the sleep and wake cycle.

Complete the exercises below.

2. Name three ways you can try to maintain balance in your life during puberty and adolescence.

a. _____ **b.** _____ **c.** _____

3. When does adolescence occur? _____

4. When does puberty occur? _____

5. What system works along with the endocrine system to regulate body functions?

_____

6. Describe how the endocrine system works.

_____

_____

_____

Name _____

Chapter 13 Review, continued

7. Label the following parts on the diagram below: *epidermis*, *dermis*, *hair*, *sweat gland*, *sebaceous gland*, *fatty cells*

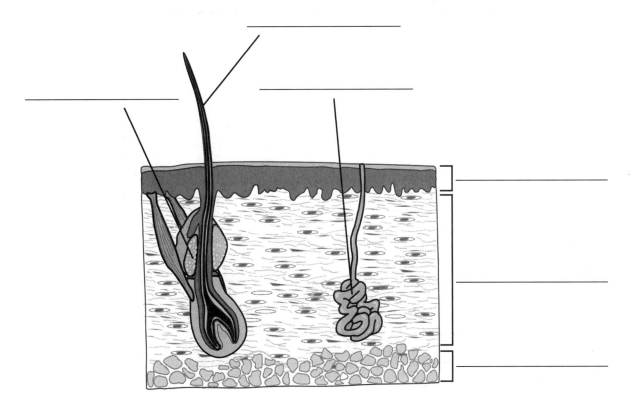

Write in the blank the word that best completes each sentence.

8. Skin is the largest _____ in the body.

9. Protecting the inside of the body is one of the main _____ of skin.

10. The _____ supports and strengthens the top layer of skin.

11. _____ is a product of the sweat glands.

12. Skin produces _____ when exposed to sunlight.

13. One very important thing you can do to take care of your skin is to _____.

14. Sebaceous glands release more _____ during puberty.

15. The endocrine system, _____, _____, _____, and

_____ all affect the growth and weight of adolescents.

16. Bones need _____ to develop properly.

17. Which gland produces the growth hormone? _____

Name _____

Chapter 13 Review, continued

18. Draw a tooth and its structures in the box. Label the illustration with the following:
enamel, dentin, pulp, crown, root, gum

[ ]

19. List the four main types of teeth.

a. _____ **c.** _____

b. _____ **d.** _____

20. Describe how a cavity forms.

_____

_____

_____

21. Name three things you can do to prevent tooth decay.

a. _____ **b.** _____ **c.** _____

22. Explain how the sleep cycle works using the name of the correct gland and the words *light* and *dark*.

_____

_____

_____

_____

23. About how many hours of sleep do adolescents need each night?

_____

Name _____

Malfunctions

Work with your group to complete the following exercises:

1. List items your group members have owned that have broken down or malfunctioned. Each person should suggest at least one thing.

Item	Owner's Name
_____	_____
_____	_____
_____	_____
_____	_____
_____	_____
_____	_____

2. Record whether or not each item was fixed and if so, how or by whom it was repaired.

Item	Details About Its Repair
_____	_____
_____	_____
_____	_____
_____	_____
_____	_____
_____	_____

3. Name at least two ways disease compares to objects that break down.

a. _____

b. _____

c. _____ (optional)

4. List diseases that your group members would like to research further.

Diseases

_____	_____
_____	_____
_____	_____

Name _____

Leprosy

Read the paragraphs below and then complete the exercises.

Throughout history, disease has been greatly misunderstood. This is partly due to a lack of scientific knowledge and partially to fear of the unknown. People who have suffered from a disease have often been isolated or mistreated in society. The Greek words *leprous* and *leprodis* were once used to describe various skin diseases. Those who suffered from leprosy were called *lepers* and were made outcasts. They often had skin sores, or lesions. Lepers typically became blind, and their feet and hands became deformed. Family, friends, and neighbors were afraid to have contact with them for fear of catching the disease. Lepers were required to call out, "Unclean! Unclean!" as they walked down the street. Very little was known about leprosy for many centuries. Some people incorrectly thought that those afflicted with this disease were cursed by God.

Leprosy, once considered only a skin disease, affects the nervous system and the membranes of the nose, throat, and eyes. Its cause is a bacterial infection. In 1874, Norwegian physician Gerhard H. Armauer Hansen identified and described the specific bacterium that causes leprosy. Although leprosy spreads mostly through nasal fluids and skin sores, it is not highly contagious.

There is great hope for leprosy patients today. Scientists have developed medicines that can cure infected people. After taking a few doses of antibiotics, a person becomes noninfectious and can return to his or her family and friends. Many countries still work to eliminate this disease: India, Brazil, China, Nepal, Madagascar, Indonesia, the Philippines, and several in Africa. The number of people who contract leprosy continues to decrease yearly. Since 1995, the World Health Organization has been trying to get rid of leprosy by offering free treatment and accurate information.

1. Name two incorrect ideas people had (and may still have in parts of the world) about leprosy.

a._____   b. _____

2. The physician who identified the bacterium that causes leprosy was _____.

3. The hands and feet of a leprosy patient can become _____ if the disease is not treated.

4. Circle all letters that are correct: Leprosy affects **a)** the skin **b)** the nose, throat, and eyes **c)** the nervous system.

5. Deformity and disfigurement of the bodies of leprosy patients can be prevented by

using _____.

Name _____

Infectious Diseases Data Table

Listed below are some common infectious diseases that affect humans. Work with a partner to fill in the missing data. Use your science textbook, encyclopedias, the Internet, or any other resources to find the necessary information.

name of disease	age group most affected by disease: (A) adults, (C) children, or (B) both	main symptom or part of the body affected by the disease	list: (P) vaccine to prevent, (D) drugs to treat or cure disease, (B) both, or (N) neither	transmission to humans: (A) animal or (H) human contact	type of pathogen usually causing disease: (V) virus, (B) bacteria, (F) fungi, (P) protist
African sleeping sickness					
chicken pox					
tuberculosis (TB)					
severe acute respiratory syndrome (SARS)					
thrush					

Name _____

Viral Replication

Use the information from the Infectious Diseases lesson in your science textbook to write captions describing how a virus attaches to a cell to make copies of itself.

_____ ➊
_____
_____
_____

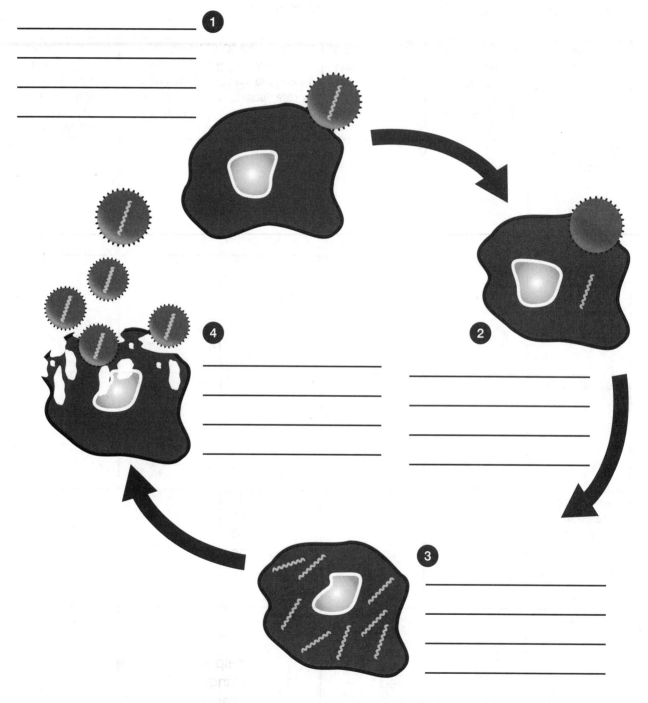

➍

➋
_____
_____
_____
_____

➌
_____
_____
_____
_____

Name _____

Analyzing Diseases

Read the description of each disease below. Determine whether it is an infectious or noninfectious disease. Explain how you know. If it is a genetic disorder or an allergy, include that information in your answer.

1. Scarlet fever is caused by the same bacteria that lead to strep throat. Symptoms include a bright red rash, fever of 38°C (101°F) or more, difficulty in swallowing, and a headache. The bacteria are spread when an infected person coughs or sneezes or touches other objects with unclean hands.

_____

_____

2. Ringworm is characterized by a scaly patch of skin. The patch may be lighter in the center, which gives the appearance of a ring. It may become very itchy and uncomfortable. The ringworm fungi feed on the outer layer of skin, hair, and nails. The most common source of ringworm is other people.

_____

_____

3. The ultimate cause of Alzheimer's disease is unknown. There is evidence, however, of dominant mutations in three different genes. Alzheimer's is a brain disorder that causes problems with memory and the ability to think. Alzheimer's affects mostly the elderly.

_____

_____

4. Cystic fibrosis is an inherited disease that affects the production of mucus, sweat, saliva, and digestive juices. These fluids, which are usually thin and slippery, become thick and sticky. This plugs up tubes, ducts, and passageways. The pancreas and lungs are particularly affected. Respiratory failure is the most dangerous result of cystic fibrosis.

_____

_____

5. From late May to the end of June in the Northern Hemisphere, many people suffer from hay fever. It is characterized by runny nose, sneezing, and itchy eyes. Hay fever is actually caused by the pollens of various seasonal plants, not the cutting of hay.

_____

_____

Name _____

Knowing the Difference

Fill in the blanks with the words from the Word Bank that correctly complete the sentences. Use each term only once.

Word Bank			
acute	chicken pox	flu	infectious
allergens	chronic	food, soil, and water	mutations
allergies	contagious	fungi	noninfectious
arthritis	contaminated objects	genetic disorders	pathogens
asthma	direct contact	immune	protists
cancer	environment	infected animals	strep throat

1. _____, such as bacteria and viruses, cause 2. _____

diseases. 3. _____ and 4. _____ also cause

diseases that are contagious. Many infectious diseases are 5. _____

because they come on suddenly and last a short time. These types of diseases can be

passed or spread by 6._____, 7. _____,

8. _____, and 9._____.

Three examples of infectious diseases are 10. _____,

11._____, and 12._____.

13. _____ diseases, on the other hand, cannot be spread

from person to person so they are not considered to be 14. _____.

Many of these diseases are 15. _____ because they can last

for long periods of time. 16. _____ are noninfectious

diseases that can be inherited. These types of disorders are caused by

17. _____ in genes or changes in chromosomes. Another type of disease

that is not contagious is 18. _____. They are caused by

19. _____, which can be anything from pollen to food. This

type of disease affects the 20. _____ system. The

21. _____ also plays a role in noninfectious diseases. Three examples

of noninfectious diseases are 22._____,

23. _____, and 24. _____.

Name _____

Systems of Defense

Label the parts of the immune and lymphatic systems below.

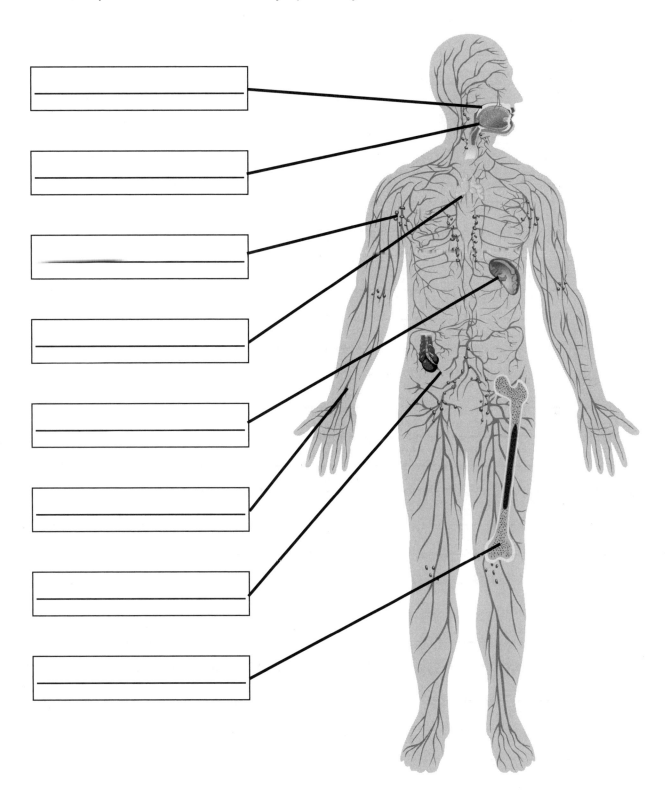

14.5B
NOTEBOOK

Name _____

Attack and Destroy

Explain the function(s) of the following:

1. lymphatic system: _____

_____

2. lymph nodes: _____

_____

3. thymus: _____

_____

4. spleen: _____

_____

5. tonsils: _____

_____

6. antibodies: _____

_____

7. List three functions of the white blood cells.

   a. _____

   b. _____

   c. _____

8. Why do lymph nodes sometimes become swollen when you get sick?

_____

_____

9. What causes a fever? _____

_____

_____

10. What are the three main ways in which the body defends itself from invaders?

   a. _____

   b. _____

   c. _____

© *Science Level 5 • Disease*

Name _____

Disease History

The data charts below show the estimated number of cases of four different diseases in the United States. On **BLM 14.6A Tracking Diseases**, plot line graphs for the data given. Start by drawing and labeling the axes. Decide the best intervals to use for each set of data. Answer the exercises after you have plotted the data on the four graphs.

Polio	
year	number of cases
1952	21,000
1953	17,500
1954	18,000
1955	5,000
1956	2,500
1957	5,500
1958	3,000
1959	6,000
1960	2,000
1961	1,000
1962	500

Tetanus	
year	number of cases
1947	570
1948	600
1949	580
1950	495
1951	500
1952	495
1953	500
1954	510
1955	450
1956	450
1957	440

Mumps	
year	number of cases
1968	90,000
1969	49,000
1970	54,000
1971	65,000
1972	38,000
1973	37,000
1974	30,000
1975	29,500
1976	18,000
1977	10,000
1978	8,000

Measles (Rubeola)	
year	number of cases
1962	480,000
1963	380,000
1964	450,000
1965	300,000
1966	200,000
1967	50,000
1968	20,000
1969	21,000
1970	48,000
1971	75,000
1972	30,000

Name _____

Spreading Germs

Observe your teacher perform four demonstrations about how infectious diseases spread. After each demonstration, complete the exercises for that demonstration.

Demonstration 1

1. This demonstration represents which of the four ways that pathogens can be spread?

_____

2. Was the contact direct or indirect? _____

3. Make a general statement about how pathogens can be passed in this manner.

_____

Demonstration 2

1. How were the pathogens spread in this demonstration? _____

2. Was the contact direct or indirect? _____

3. Make a general statement about how pathogens can be passed according to this

demonstration. _____

4. How could you prevent the spread of disease in these last two demonstrations?

_____

Demonstration 3

1. How were the pathogens contracted? _____

2. Was the contact direct or indirect? _____

3. Make a conclusion about the spread of pathogens. _____

_____

Demonstration 4

1. This demonstration represents that pathogens can be spread by

_____

2. How can you prevent the spread of disease in this manner?

_____

Name _____

History of Pathology

Read the paragraph below and complete the exercises.

Pathology is the study of diseases and how they affect the body. Dr. Rudolf Virchow (1821–1902), a prominent German physician, is considered *the Father of Pathology*. Dr. Virchow's extensive work led to a better understanding of hundreds of diseases. During his lifetime he wrote over 2,000 books and papers on the subject of pathology. By the age of 25, Virchow had already discovered and named many types of tumors and cells. He was the first person to recognize leukemia and certain symptoms of stomach cancer. He established and described many terms in pathology and is credited for writing the first descriptions of fungal diseases. In 1859, he published a book named *Cell Pathology* that became the foundation for the microscopic study of disease. Additionally, Dr. Virchow was active in his community and devoted to political and social reform.

1. How does pathology relate to what you have learned in this chapter?

_____

_____

2. Why do you think Virchow is referred to as the "Father of Pathology?"

_____

_____

_____

_____

3. List three of Virchow's accomplishments.

  a. _____

  b. _____

  c. _____

4. Look in the Cell Structure lesson of Chapter 3 to read about another very important contribution that Virchow made to science that is not included in the paragraph above. Tell what the contribution was and include the page number(s) where the

information is located. _____

_____

_____

Name _____

Acquiring Immunity

1. Organize the following terms and complete the concept map below.

Word Bank

immune response	antibodies come from another source	by vaccination
lasts years to a lifetime	by having the disease	memory cells
by injecting antibodies	lasts a few months	comes from mother
body makes own antibodies		

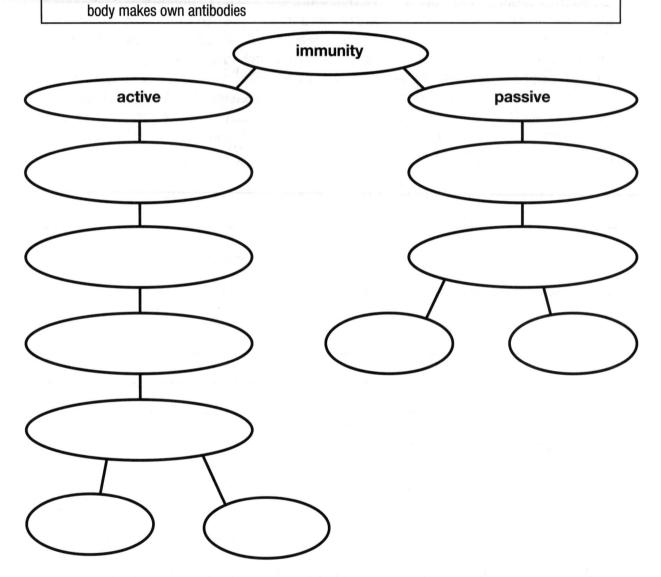

2. What role do memory cells play in active immunity?

_____

_____

_____

Name _____

Vocabulary Review

Match the clues at the bottom of the page to the vocabulary words in the drawings.
Write the letter of the clue on the blank underneath each term.

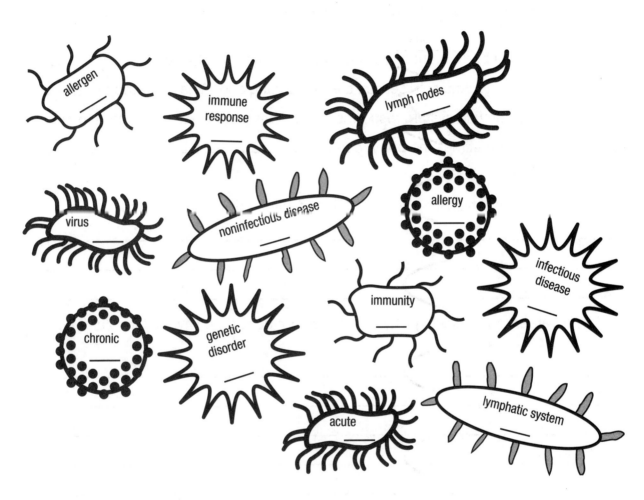

a. a disease that is not contagious

b. lasting for a long time or recurring frequently

c. an abnormal reaction to a foreign substance

d. the steps taken by the immune system when invaded by pathogens

e. the ability to protect against a pathogen before getting sick

f. areas that filter lymph and trap pathogens

g. a noncontagious disease that is usually inherited

h. something that causes an allergy

i. a nonliving microscopic particle that often causes disease

j. beginning suddenly and lasting for a short time

k. a disease that is contagious and is caused by a pathogen

l. is part of the immune system and helps fight pathogens

Name _____

Chapter 14 Review

Complete the following exercises. Fill in the blanks below with the correct terms.

1. When a pathogen enters the body, the series of events during the immune response is similar to a chain reaction. Complete **BLM 14.8B Chain Reaction** by organizing the steps the body takes to fight pathogens.

2. When the human body is out of balance and becomes ill, it has a _____.

3. _____ cause diseases that are contagious. When a pathogen enters the body, the immune system responds by activating the white blood cells to fight the infection. Sometimes the body receives _____ _____ after this happens.

4. List three ways in which infectious and noninfectious diseases are alike.

   a. _____

   b. _____

   c. _____

5. Write a paragraph explaining why viruses are not considered living things and how they multiply.

   _____

   _____

   _____

   _____

   _____

6. Name two types of noninfectious diseases. Explain how a person could get each disease.

   a. _____

     _____

   b. _____

     _____

7. List eight components of the immune and lymphatic systems.

   _____

   _____